The Illustrated Ramayana

A Wilco Book
Outstanding works of universal interest

The Illustrated RAMAYANA

ISBN:978-81-8252-228-5

Published by;
Wilco
Publishing House
ITTS House, 33 Sri Saibaba Marg
Off Rampart Row, Kalaghoda, Fort,
Mumbai 400 001, India.

Tel: (91-22) 2204 1420 / 2284 2574
Fax: (91-22) 2204 1429
E mail:wilcos@vsnl.com

CONTENTS

The Birth of Four Princes

The great King Dasharatha of Ayodhya was the grandson of Raghu, of the Surya Vansha, the greatest of Emperors, who gave all that belonged to him in charity, except the clothes on his body. Dasharatha was as noble and wise a king as his grandfather. He possessed all the virtues of his ancestors and was kind, generous and strong. King Dasharatha's empire, with his capital city, Ayodhya, was vast and lush with forests and rivers and stretched right up to the river Ganga.

His kingdom was prosperous, his subjects did not lack anything and were happy to be ruled by a noble king such as Dasharatha. The king had more wealth than Kubera and Indra put together and he was as learned as a Maharishi. His people prospered under his kind and generous rule. Many a sage made his hermitage in the kingdom of King Dasharatha and he was known to be pious and god-fearing. He prayed to the sun god Surya everyday and was very content.

The only regret in the King's heart was that he did not have any children of his own. Not one of his three Queens, Kaushalya, Sumitra or Kaikeyi had borne him any children and this saddened him very much. He wanted a son who would carry on the glorious Raghu tradition and rule his kingdom just as wisely and well as himself. So he conferred with his rishis and ministers and they decided to invite Sage Rishyashringa to perform a yajna to beget a child.

All the preparations were done and as the powerful yajna was being performed in Ayodhya, the Devas in heaven were discussing King Dasharatha's plight. The Devas went to Lord Vishnu and humbly requested him to be born to Dasharatha as four sons. So Lord Vishnu sent a Deva down to Ayodhya, who emerged from the flames of the holy fire, handed over a golden pot of kheer to the noble King Dasharatha and said, "The Devas have heard your prayers and Lord Vishnu is pleased with your sacrifice. He has granted you this pot of kheer for your wives. Let them partake of it and they will surely bear you four sons."

The King was overjoyed and he carried the golden pot of kheer to his palace. The joy of his three Queens knew no bounds when they heard this news. They were excited at the prospect of having children. Now Kaushalya was the eldest and so the King gave her half of the kheer. The other half was divided amongst the younger Queens, Sumitra and Kaikeyi.

Since Kaikeyi was the last to receive the kheer she was enraged and she started cursing and complaining. Lord Shankara's eagle swooped down from the heavens, snatched off the kheer that was in Kaikeyi's hands, and flew away to humiliate her for her lack of grace.

On a mountain named Anjan, faraway, sat a devotee of Lord Shankara named Anjani who had been in meditation for many years. The eagle dropped the kheer into the open hands of Anjani and flew away. Kaikeyi was furious at having lost her share of the kheer. To pacify her, the other two Queens shared their kheer with her.

Soon enough, by the grace of Lord Vishnu the three Queens became pregnant. There was a joy like no other in the entire kingdom. The King truly had no regrets now. He at once set out to meet his guru, the noble Sage Vashishta. He bowed down to touch the feet of his guru and get his blessings and tell him the happy news.

Vashishta was pleased and he advised the King that during the time the three Queens were pregnant, he should fulfil all their wishes without any hesitation and keep them happy.

The King was only too pleased to carry out the advice of his guru and set out to serve his wives and attend to them. Everyone in the kingdom waited for the day that the four princes would be born. The three Queens spent all their time in the palace and its lush gardens in anticipation of the great day. The face of the King lit up with joy as he walked with his pregnant wives in the gardens of the palace.

It was noon on the seventh day of the month of Chaitra and the sun was high in the sky. On this auspicious day the three Queens gave birth to their four sons. Kaushalya, the eldest Queen of King Dasharatha, gave birth to Rama, Kaikeyi to Bharatha and Sumitra to the twins, Lakshmana and Shatrughna. The whole kingdom joined them in a celebration as never before witnessed. There was much joy on the faces of the three Queens as they saw their sons moving their tiny hands and legs and opening their eyes for the first time.

The four Princes cried and laughed lustily, making their parents glad. Not only was the King joyous, he was also relieved to now have four sons. With happiness in his heart he looked at the children as they lay in their mothers' laps. The King vowed to give them the best education and training and make them into strapping lads and princes. He knew that the future of his dynasty and his kingdom, lay in these tiny hands!

When thirteen days had passed since the birth of the four Princes, King Dasharatha invited his guru, the noble Sage Vashishta to perform a ceremony to name the newborn Princes. The Sage was overjoyed to perform the task and he once again reminded himself that these were no ordinary Princes. He knew that they were Lord Vishnu who had been reincarnated as the four sons of Dasharatha.

Sage Vashishta made elaborate and grand preparations for the naming ceremony. Flowers were brought from all over the kingdom. The generous King gave away gold and jewels to his subjects. At the ceremony, Sage Vashishta sat in the middle while the other rishis surrounded him. The King and his wives, with their children, sat close to the Sage. Taking each baby into his arms the Sage blessed him and whispered his name into his ear. Kaushalya's son was named Rama, the bringer of joy and peace, Kaikeyi's son Bharatha, the supporter of the universe, and Sumitra's sons were named Lakshmana, the soul of noble virtues and Shatrughna, the destroyer of all enemies.

As the four Princes grew up, King Dasharatha and the Queens devoted all their time to the four boys. They gloried in their little pranks, enjoyed their lisping talk, and answered all their inquisitive questions. There was peace and happiness like never before in the palace and in the kingdom.

The King spent all his time and energy in teaching the boys and nurturing them with love and affection. They were educated in all the ways befitting a prince.

They were encouraged to play in the gardens and in the palace. They played with one another and with all the birds and beasts on the palace grounds. It was a blissful time. Under the watchful eyes of their father and their mothers they became young lads. The subjects loved the four Princes just as much as they loved their kind King.

King Dasharatha was an accomplished warrior of many skills. He was a skilled archer who could shoot at anything by just hearing the sounds it produced. So he made it a point to teach his sons how to become archers. The four boys were quick to learn and soon they were as good as their father.

The King's chest swelled with pride as he watched the four boys display their skills. By now the four Princes had nearly attained adolescence and were very skilled with their swords and their bows. The once childless King Dasharatha was overjoyed with his four sons and their progress. He now felt that they were ready to pursue their formal education and become learned and wise.

He knew that when they had gained knowledge, they would also know right from wrong, in the glorious tradition of the Raghu Dynasty.

The Slaying of Tadaka

When all the four Princes attained adolescence, King Dasharatha decided that the time was right to send them to the hermitage of his guru, the noble Sage Vashishta, for their formal education. They were sent to the Sage where they learnt quickly, had soon mastered the Vedas and had complete knowledge in the administration of a kingdom and in the other disciplines required of a prince. They learnt the law of the land govern the same and pass verdicts. The Sage was happy when they assimilated all the knowledge quickly and was pleased at their natural tendency towards the good and the just.

The Princes spent a lot of their time in meditation which made their intellect grow sharper. Their education was coming to an end and soon it was time for them to return to the palace. The Princes bowed at the feet of their guru, the noble Sage Vashishta. He blessed them to be great and wise rulers, to put his teachings to practice and bring glory to their dynasty and their ancestors.

Meanwhile, the noble Sage Vashishta had sent word to the palace, asking the King to send courtiers to escort the young Princes back to the palace. King Dasharatha sent Sumantra, his wisest and most trusted minister to fetch them. He also sent with him four of his finest robes for the Princes to wear.

Sumantra reached the hermitage of the noble Sage and bowed down at his feet to get his blessings. After blessing him, Vashishta enquired about the welfare of King Dasharatha and his three Queens and subjects. Then he sent for the four Princes.

The Princes donned their royal robes, crowns and jewellery. Before mounting their chariot, they bowed down in the direction of the hermitage out of respect. Though they were sad to leave the place that had been their second home for many years, they controlled their emotions, just as their wise guru had taught them. Sumantra led the procession back to the palace in a golden chariot, befitting the sons of Dasharatha.

The horses driving the chariot were the finest and the swiftest of the palace and soon they neared the gates of the city of Ayodhya. The people of Ayodhya had gathered to witness the return of the Princes. The entire city was decorated and there was celebration everywhere. People from all across the kingdom had come to welcome them back. They realised that this was the end of an important phase in the Princes' lives and the beginning of a new one, which would lead them into their adult life. The Princes were elated at this grand welcome.

When the procession arrived at the palace, the four Princes made their way to their father and mothers. They bowed down and touched their mothers' feet to get their blessings. With tears of joy in their eyes, the three Queens embraced their sons for the first time in many years. The Princes then proceeded to bow down to their father and touched his feet. The King's joy knew no bounds. Here were his beloved sons who had grown into fine young men.

Rama was declared crown Prince and he led his brothers in the matters of the state and government. He was a just and wise Prince and listened patiently before he made any decisions. As the King sat on his throne and watched, he was proud that his sons had grown up, and awaited the day Rama would take his place on the throne as King. One day as King Dasharatha sat on his throne thinking, the arrival of the great Sage Vishwamitra was announced. The Sage was respected and held in awe for his immense knowledge of the Vedas by one and all including the Sages of the kingdom.

As the sage entered, the King arose to greet him and bowed down to get his blessings. Sage Vishwamitra was pleased. He blessed the King, sat down to speak with him and said, "I have been trying to perform a yajna for sometime but have been unsuccessful, as two powerful demons called Mareecha and Subahu ruin the yajna by throwing bones and blood into the sacrificial fire. Please send the eldest of your sons, Rama, to kill the demons and help me perform the yajna."

The King was afraid to send Rama into the forest to fight the demons, but another noble sage, Sage Vashishta, reassured him and asked him to send not just Rama but also Lakshmana with them. Vashishta reminded the King that the great Sage Vishwamitra was quite capable of protecting Rama and Lakshmana from any danger with his spiritual powers and that the two Princes would be safe with him. So Rama and Lakshmana accompanied Sage Vishwamitra into the forest.

They crossed over to the other side of the holy river Ganga and made their way deep into the forest. Though many a terrifying beast roared from the forest, Rama and Lakshmana rode bravely. Their bows were strung and ready, to shoot down any beasts or demons that emerged from the forest. Many years ago, people had lived in peace in this very same forest called Dandaka, until the time that the demons had driven them out and occupied it.

Sage Vishwamitra had warned the Princes that the demons Subahu, Mareecha and Tadaka were living deep in the forest and that no one dared to enter. The entire forest had become a wilderness because of the dreadful demons and their horrendous deeds.

He added that Tadaka, the she-demon possessed the strength of a thousand elephants and she loved to kill and eat people. Her atrocities were intolerable. Killing her was the only way to make the Dandaka forest safe for the Sages and the people to live in once again.

After listening very carefully to what the great Sage Vishwamitra had said, Rama took his mighty bow and twanged it in order to frighten Tadaka and make her appear. The twang of the bow resounded in the whole forest and the earth shook at the mighty sound.

As soon as Tadaka heard the mighty twang of the bow, she roused herself from her lair and came running towards the sound. Her rage was fierce and she wanted to kill the person who had disturbed her in her own abode.

She saw Rama, Lakshmana and the great Sage Vishwamitra and was pleased because she was quite hungry. She thought that the two young boys and the wise Sage would be no match for her demonic skills. She thought she would kill them and that they would make a fine meal.

She ran forward towards Rama. A great battle ensued. The demoness was truly powerful and strong and put up a great fight. But she was no match for the fighting skills of the two Princes. Finally, Rama mounted an arrow on his bow and shot it straight into her chest, felling her. The ugly demoness fell and the forest floor shook under their feet. All the animals ran helter-skelter and the birds made a dreadful noise.

There was a cheer from the Devas in heaven as they had been watching this fight from the beginning. Even the great Sage Vishwamitra was amazed at the skills of the two Princes. He embraced and blessed them and was proud that they had been victorious.

The great Sage Vishwamitra now had nothing to worry about and conducted his yagna without any disruption. There was peace in the forest once more. The animals returned, the birds chirped happily, the streams became sweet and the grass grew green and lush. The mighty Rama and his brave brother Lakshmana had rid the forest of the demons and brought peace to the jungle once again.

Rama Weds Sita

After the great Sage Vishwamitra had performed the yajna in the forest of Dandaka with Rama and Lakshmana protecting him, he led the Princes towards the great city of Mithila. The city was ruled by the famous King Janaka who was conducting a Swayamvara for the marriage of his beautiful daughter Sita. The Sage wanted the two Princes to witness the Swayamvara.

On the way they came across a beautiful but deserted hermitage where Sage Gautama had once lived with his lovely wife Ahalya. Ahalya was a vain woman and so the God Indra disguised himself as the Sage and entered the hut in an attempt to possess her. When Sage Gautama found out, he cursed Ahalya to become a stone and live only on air until the time that Lord Rama visited the hermitage.

As soon as Rama set foot on the stone, the curse was lifted and Ahalya stood before them with tears in her eyes. She thanked Rama for freeing her from the curse.

The two Princes and the Sage then proceeded towards Mithila, the capital of the kind and wise king, Videha Janaka. The King was known as Videha Janaka because he possessed the ability to forget the demands of his body at will. As soon as King Janaka saw the great Sage Vishwamitra and the two Princes, he ran out to welcome them, as he knew the Sage well. He asked the Sage who the Princes were? The Sage replied that they were the sons of the great King Dasharatha of Ayodhya and they had come with him to witness the Swayamvara of Princess Sita.

King Janaka was overjoyed and welcomed them with open arms. The palace had been richly decorated for the event and it was truly beautiful. A number of royal seats had been arranged in a courtyard. At the centre was a pedestal and there rested upon it, the mighty bow of Lord Shiva. Janaka's condition was that the warrior who could string the bow would marry the beautiful and virtuous Sita.

The next morning there was a huge gathering of princes and kings from all parts of India who had assembled in Mithila to try and win the hand of Princess Sita. They were all seated in the royal courtyard as they waited for the Swayamvara to begin. The beautiful Princess Sita, came out in her wedding robes and was seated with due respect. She was so beautiful, the entire place glowed with her beauty.

King Janaka announced the beginning of the Swayamvara. One by one the princes and kings came forward, as their names and those of their forefathers were announced. They then proceeded towards the bow and tried stringing it but some could not even lift it! Others buckled under it! Not one valiant prince or brave king could budge the mighty bow of Lord Shiva. King Janaka watched with bated breath as each warrior stepped forth and tried but failed, his head hung in shame. King Janaka's heart sank. If all failed, then who would marry his virtuous daughter?

The great Sage Vishwamitra, Rama and Lakshmana were also watching this sad spectacle. King Janaka was losing all hope, so he got up and addressed the princes and kings who had gathered. He said, "Is there no hero left on earth? Is there no one who can lift the bow of Lord Shiva? Is it my daughter's fate that she will never be married?"

"I am ashamed to see that not one person has even succeeded in lifting the bow not to speak of stringing it!" The sorrow and hopelessness in the King's voice touched every heart.

But none of the princes and kings could do anything. They sat on their royal seats, their heads hung in shame. They had all tried and failed abjectly.

The entire courtyard was silent. The anguish of the King, the shame of the princes and kings, the sorrow of Sita and her maids was more than evident.

While Janaka's words had caused shame and anguish in the hearts of the warriors gathered, Lakshmana was enraged. He thought that when his mighty brother Rama, the divine and the virtuous, was present, King Janaka should never have said what he did. Did he not know that there was nothing Rama could not do? Sage Vishwamitra sensed the rage that was building up in Lakshmana's heart and he knew what the best course of action would be. He asked Rama to go and try stringing the bow. He said to Rama, "O valiant Prince, son of Dasharatha, I have complete faith in your abilities. Go and win the hand of the fair Sita, for she was always destined to be yours." Rama rose, bowed down at the Sage's feet in respect, and walked towards the pedestal on which the bow was placed. Every eye was on him.

As Rama approached the bow, he bowed down to it. Janaka was amazed. None of the other warriors had shown respect to the mighty bow of Lord Shiva. Then Rama bent and held the bow like a god. All those gathered watched in pin-drop silence. Without any effort, the glorious Raghu Prince picked up the bow like a toy. Resting one end of the bow on his toe he bent and strung it with ease.

Then he drew the string back with so much force that the mighty bow broke into two at the middle emitting a thunderous sound. This caused an uproar with the gods cheering from above and the applauding of the Kings and Princes who were gathered there.

King Janaka and Sita were delighted that Rama had not only strung the bow but also broken it with his divine might. Sita had found her true husband, the brave and mighty Rama, for whom she had been destined.

King Janaka rose and asked his beautiful and virtuous daughter to garland Rama. Sita made her way towards Rama and garlanded him to indicate that she would wed him. Witnessing the garlanding of Rama, the gods and devas showered flowers from heaven. Great sages, Princes and Kings gathered at the Swayamwara, bestowed their blessings with shouts of victory. Word was then sent to the great King Dasharatha in Ayodhya that his son Rama had won the hand of the lovely Princess Sita by breaking Lord Shiva's mighty bow.

With a large number of his subjects, King Dasharatha proceeded to the city of Mithila for the wedding. He took with him gold and jewels and fine horses as gifts for King Janaka. It was a grand procession that followed the King as he made his way to the city of Mithila. There were dancers and musicians and many elephants and men dressed in royal robes. As the great King Dasharatha reached the gates of the palace at Mithila, King Janaka welcomed him warmly.

The marriage was performed with much pomp and splendour. Everyone present was full of joy. During the festivities Vishwamitra and Vashishta also asked for the hands of the two daughters of King Janaka's brother Kushadhwaja - Mandavi and Shruthakirthi for Bharatha and Shatrughna. Janaka also offered his younger daughter Urmila to Lakshmana. After the royal wedding of the four Princes, Janaka bade a tearful farewell to all the daughters. Though he was sad that they were leaving him, he was also happy that they had all found such virtuous and brave husbands.

The wedding procession then made its way towards Ayodhya. The people of Ayodhya lined the streets and showered flowers in the path of the brides and the grooms. There was celebration in the air and the joy in the people's hearts knew no bounds. Their beloved Princes had brought back brides who would be the pride of the land.

The Exile of Rama

After the return of the Princes from Mithila there was peace in the kingdom of Ayodhya. The great King Dasharatha ruled over Ayodhya for twelve years and the kingdom prospered. One day, Bharatha and Shatrughna's maternal uncle came to Ayodhya and took his two nephews to his kingdom, Kaikeya. Soon King Dasharatha, aware that he was getting old wished to crown his eldest son, Rama, as the King.

The King sought the advice of Sage Vashishta on this issue, who was glad to hear about the King's intention. He advised King Dasharatha that he should also seek the approval of all the members of the royal court.

When the entire court was assembled, the King announced his decision to crown Rama. The courtiers were only too happy and agreed with their King. Rama was loved and respected by all the people of Ayodhya and they all felt that he deserved to be crowned.

After having sought the approval of his courtiers, King Dasharatha asked his minister Sumantra to fetch Rama, who was still unaware of the happenings. On arriving Rama bowed down and touched his father's feet in order to get his blessings. The King embraced him and said, "Dear son, I have become old and it is time for someone to take my place on the throne. So I have decided to crown you."

As the crowning was to take place the next day, Rama visited Sage Vashishta to seek his blessings and advice. The Sage told the Prince that he must observe a fast along with his wife Sita through the night. Rama promised to abide by his advice and practiced penance that night.

All the three Queens of King Dasharatha were also delighted by the news. They all loved Rama dearly. However, Manthara, the maid of queen Kaikeyi had already begun brewing trouble for Rama. She told Kaikeyi that if Rama were to become the king he would enslave Bharatha and might even kill him. Love for her own son clouded Kaikeyi's judgement and she paid heed to Manthara's evil words.

Kaikeyi was so taken up by what Manthara had said, that she herself became overcome with evil thoughts. Manthara added fuel to the fire by saying that Rama would drive them all out and have them killed. Kaikeyi asked Manthara what she should do. Manthara reminded her of the two wishes that Dasharatha had granted her when she had saved him on the battlefield and that the time had come for the Queen to claim the two boons. She advised her to lie down in the protest chamber until King Dasharatha came to see her.

Corrupted by Manthara's evil words and blinded by the love for her son, Kaikeyi went to the protest chamber. As soon as the King heard about Kaikeyi's state, he rushed to her. The Queen had removed all her jewels and had dressed shabbily. The King pleaded with her to tell him what she wanted but she remained silent. At last, the King swore in the name of Rama that he would do whatever she wanted him to. Upon hearing this, the Queen said, "My first wish is that you crown my son Bharatha and my second wish is that you exile Rama to live in the forest for fourteen years." King Dasharatha was completely shattered at her demands and fell down unconscious.

During the course of these events, Rama and the beautiful Sita were sitting in their palace looking forward to his coronation as King. Having fasted the whole night upon the advice of the noble Sage Vashishta, they were talking about how the events of the day would unfold.

Meanwhile, the great King Dasharatha, who was very distraught after hearing his Queen's demands, was now pleading with her to change her mind. He said, "How can I send Rama to live in the forest when I told him only yesterday that I was going to crown him King? How will he live in the forest for fourteen years? Have pity on me in my old age for I will not be able to live a moment without Rama!" The more the King pleaded and begged his Queen to change her mind, the more she would not relent and remained adamant as ever.

Seeing that the unrelenting Kaikeyi would not yield, King Dasharatha, having to keep his word, finally said, "Fine! It will be as you wish, but you will tell Rama yourself." Happily, Kaikeyi sent Sumantra to fetch Rama.

Rama was getting ready for his coronation when Sumantra asked him to come to the main palace as Queen Kaikeyi and King Dasharatha had requested his presence. Rama hastened to obey. As he entered he saw Queen Kaikeyi in old clothes, bereft of all her jewels, and his father distraught with tears in his eyes. He bowed down at his father's feet and then standing with folded hands before Queen Kaikeyi, he humbly asked her what she wanted of him and why she had requested his presence.

The Queen narrated to him about how his father had granted her two boons long ago and which she had redeemed last night. She continued, "First, I want my son Bharatha to be crowned King and secondly, I want you to go to the forest in exile for fourteen years." Rama unruffled, quietly bowed down, touched her feet and declared that he was ready to carry out her wishes and was also happy about the crowning of Bharatha as the King.

As Rama prepared to go to the forest, his beautiful wife Sita and his dear brother Lakshmana also prepared to go with him. The three then fell at the feet of the distressed King and sought his blessings, after which, they also seeked the blessings of the three Queens.

By this time news had spread throughout Ayodhya that Rama was going to the forest in exile as per the wishes of Queen Kaikeyi. A big crowd gathered outside the palace. The gathering consisted of men, women and children of all ages and they had all decided to leave their homes and join Rama to live with him in the forest.

As it was not appropriate to go to the forest in their royal robes, Rama, Lakshmana and Sita had donned the clothes of hermits and discarded all their jewellery. They mounted their chariot to leave and all the people gathered there followed them with much sorrow in their hearts. Sumantra, the minister, was their charioteer.

As Rama was leaving, the King wept inconsolably and cried out Rama's name. Nobody was able to pacify him.

As Rama made his way to the forest, the chariot came to a stop on the banks of the river Tamsa. Sumantra unyoked the horses and let them have a drink of water. Rama recited his evening prayers and turning to Lakshmana, said, "Let us fast on this first night of our journey." Lakshmana spread out some grass for Rama and the virtuous Sita on which to rest for the night. He himself spent the long hours of the night in vigil, talking to Sumantra.

Long before it dawned Rama arose from his sleep and said to Sumantra, "The people of Ayodhya who have followed us so faithfully are still fast asleep. If they awake they will surely not let me go to the forest. So, harness the horses and lead us across the river so that we may leave before they wake up." When the people of Ayodhya awoke they were surprised to find that Rama, Lakshmana and Sita were nowhere to be seen and so with much sorrow in their hearts, they returned to Ayodhya.

Finally, the three of them and Sumantra reached the southern boundary of the kingdom of Kosala. Here Rama bowed in respect in the direction of his motherland Ayodhya. They then proceeded in their chariot and reached the banks of the holy and mighty river, Ganga.

Meanwhile, the ruler of the region, namely Guha, had heard that Rama was passing through. He went to Rama and said, "Please bless my land. Spend all fourteen years of your exile with us." Rama embraced Guha and replied, "I am moved by your love for me but I am bound by my promises. I must spend the fourteen years in the forest, however, I shall surely spend this night here with you." In the morning, Rama said to Sumantra, "The time has come for you to return to Ayodhya, for my father is old and grief-stricken and he needs you more than I." So, with a heavy heart, Sumantra returned to Ayodhya. Rama, Lakshmana and Sita proceeded into the forest. Thus began their fourteen years of exile in the forest.

The Boatman On The Ganges

Having sent Sumantra back to the palace, Rama, Sita and Lakshmana arrived at the banks of the holy river, Ganga. They needed to cross the river, in order to proceed further into the forest. Rama looked around and sighted a small boat a little further away from the shore. He requested the boatman to bring the boat and ferry them across the river.

As the boatman, who made his living ferrying people across the river approache, he recognised Rama. He bowed to them and said to Rama, "I know who you are. Even the dust from your feet has power enough to turn a stone into a woman. My boat is only made of wood. If you were to step into it, it would turn into something else too. Then I would not be able to feed my family, because this is my only means of livelihood. So, please pardon me. I cannot ferry you across the river."

Rama smiled at him and again requested, "My good man, my wife Sita, my brother Lakshmana and I have to get across the river." The boatman suggested, "I will take you across the river on one condition only. If you let me wash your feet of all the dust, I will let you step into my boat. For I do not want my boat to turn into a woman." The all-compassionate Rama smiled and assented. He said, "If it satisfies you, do wash my feet and then take us across." At once, the boatman ran to the river and filled a wooden basin with water. He approached Rama and knelt in front of him.

With great care, he washed the feet of the Lord and then wiped them with his upper cloth. He was grateful for this privilege and his heart was full of joy as he performed the task. The Devas looked down from heaven and envied the fact that the humble boatman had an opportunity to serve the Lord in a way that none of them could. After having washed the feet of Lord Rama, the boatman helped the three of them into his boat.

With his heart overflowing with love for the Lord, he rowed across the river, ensuring that the ride was smooth and pleasurable. When they reached the other side, the boatman jumped off the boat and helped them get off. As soon as the three of them stood safely on the shore, the boatman fell at Rama's feet and sought his blessings.

The virtuous Sita sought to reward the man for his devotion to Rama and took off a jewelled ring to give to him. The boatman refused to accept anything for his services and clung to Rama's feet. He said, "I am truly blessed, my Lord, for you have blessed me. I needed nothing else but your blessings."

The boatman then rowed away. Rama bathed in the holy river with Lakshmana. Meanwhile, Sita sought the blessings of the river Ganga for their journey forward and their stay in the forest.

Rama, Sita and Lakshmana then renewed their journey and very soon the mighty river Ganga was left far behind. Rama instructed Lakshmana to lead and said he would follow Sita, so that she would be in the middle of the two brothers and well protected from any dangers in the forest.

They walked this way through the rocks and plants on the forest floor. The Princes and the Princess of Ayodhya had never stepped on rocky ground like this. However, they took it in their stride and continued to walk until they reached the hermitage of the powerful and holy Sage Bharadwaja. He welcomed them with warmth and affection. He listened to their tale and understood the situation they were in. After much thought, he advised them that the most suitable place for them to make a home in the forest would be Chitrakoot. So, Rama heeded the Sage's advice and decided to set up their forest home in the peaceful Chitrakoot.

Meanwhile, Sumantra, his heart filled with sorrow, had made his way back to the palace in Ayodhya. King Dasharatha and Rama's mother, Queen Kaushalya were grief-stricken to see Sumantra alone. Said King Dasharatha, "Where is Rama? Didn't he come back with you? How can I live without him? Where is he, O Sumantra, where is he?"

The Queen said, "Take me to him, Sumantra. Take me to my son, so I can live with him in the forest. How will he live alone? And Lakshmana and Sita? They are but children!"

"Rama sent me back to be by your side. He has gone into the forest to fulfil Queen Kaikeyi's wishes," said Sumantra. Queen Kaushalya cried inconsolably and the King fell down on hearing these words. He held his head in his hands and cried, "I see now that nobody can escape the consequences resulting from their past actions. Once, in my youth, I had committed a horrible sin and this is my punishment now for the same."

Queen Kaushalya was puzzled and even Sumantra wanted to know just what the King meant. So the King explained, "When I was a young Prince, I was a very skilled archer and loved to hunt. I could shoot at animals just by hearing the noises they made, even without being able to see them. One night as I was hunting in the forest, I heard a gurgling sound near a river. I thought it might be an elephant drinking water at the river so I shot my arrow in the direction of the sound. To my horror thereafter, I heard a boy's cry."

"I rushed across and saw a young boy lying by the river. My arrow had found its mark and the boy was dying. He told me that he was Shravan and that he had come to fetch water for his mother to drink. Both his parents were blind and he was their sole caretaker. He asked me to take the water to his parents. So saying the boy breathed his last. When I went to the boy's parents and told them what had happened, they cursed me, that I would die grieving for my son just as they would."

King Dasharatha continued, "Their curse has haunted me ever since. And it has now come true. How will I live without my beloved Rama? Oh! I will surely die! I am in the grip of the God of Death!" The Queen and Sumantra tried to pacify him and escorted him into his chambers.

The great King then cried out to his Queen Kaushalya, who was satting by his side, "Kaushalya! I am losing my sight just like Shravan's parents. Won't Rama come to me? Will he not save me?" He then cried out Rama's name six times and breathed his last. The whole palace was plunged into sorrow and there was gloom everywhere. Queen Kaushalya was distressed by her loss. First her son had been sent away from her and now her beloved husband was no more. The noble Sage Vashishta arrived soon after he heard of the tragedy that had befallen the people of Ayodhya. Messengers were also sent to fetch Bharatha and Shatrughna.

Bharatha and Shatrughna rode to Ayodhya with a sense of foreboding that something terrible had happened. As they reached Ayodhya, Bharatha first went to his mother's palace. He sought her blessings and then enquired about his father. Upon hearing of his father's demise, Bharatha was shocked and wept bitterly. He then asked his mother about Rama. Kaikeyi narrated the entire story to Bharatha and said that she had sent Rama into exile so he, Bharatha, could become King.

Bharatha was enraged. He said to his mother, "What have you done? In your blind greed, you have murdered my father! I will no longer be your son." So saying, he stormed out of the palace and vowed to bring the virtuous Rama back, to rule Ayodhya. He swore that he would make Rama the King as per his fathers wish.

Bharatha Goes To The Forest

After hearing what had happened to Rama, Sita and Lakshmana, Bharatha disowned his mother, Queen Kaikeyi, for the unforgivable sin she had committed. He vowed to bring Rama back from the forest and reinstate him on the throne of Ayodhya. Bharatha's anger knew no bounds and inside his heart, he grieved greatly for the loss of his father. Moreover, the separation from Rama, Sita and Lakshmana pained him so much that he stormed out of the palace.

Shatrughna was equally angry and upon the sight of Manthara, he was so overcome and blinded with rage that he kicked her hard. He cursed her for poisoning Queen Kaikeyi's mind with greed of the throne for her son.

Bharatha was inconsolable and the pain of the wrong that his mother had committed vested heavily in his heart. He rushed to see his father's body lying in state in the palace chambers.

The great and wise Sages Vamadeva and Vashishta did their best to console Bharatha and Shatrughna. They said to Bharatha, "O noble Prince, have courage in your heart. Every person who is born on Earth is destined to die and leave one day for his heavenly abode. It is time for you to perform the last rites of your father, the great King Dasharatha." After much consoling, Bharatha finally rose and initiated preparations for the last rites of his father.

On the banks of the great river Sarayu, a mighty pyre made of sandalwood was raised. Bharatha consigned the body of the great and virtuous King Dasharatha to the holy flames of the all-consuming fire. He then bathed in the river and offered prayers for his father's soul. Having performed the last rites, Bharatha made his way back to the palace with sorrow in his heart, but he was determined to bring Rama back to Ayodhya.

Fourteen days had passed since Bharatha's return to Ayodhya which was now without a king. So, the ministers called an assembly and after much deliberation and thought, they decided that according to Queen Kaikeyi's wish Bharatha should be crowned King of Ayodhya.

When Bharatha heard this, he bowed down humbly to the assembly and said, "I will not be crowned king. I have vowed to bring Rama, Sita and Lakshmana back from the forest and I will have Rama crowned king according to my father's wishes."

The entire assembly was moved by Bharatha's devotion to his brother, Rama and his father and they accepted his decision gladly. Preparations were made for Bharatha to go to the forest with chariots and horses befitting a King. Many of the assembly members and the people of Ayodhya also joined Bharatha on this mission.

All the Ministers, the Sages, the people of Ayodhya and the three Queens of King Dasharatha made their way into the forest with Bharatha. A huge army also went with them to protect them from demons, robbers and wild animals. Clouds of dust rose from the ground as they marched forward and the rumbling was heard for miles.

As the multitude reached the forest, Rama, Sita and Lakshmana heard the rumbling noise. Rama asked Lakshmana to climb up a tall tree to see who was approaching. Lakshmana saw the huge army with the flags of the Raghu Vansha on the chariots and was alarmed because he thought that Bharatha was coming to attack them. He prepared for combat but Rama told him to stay calm and rest assured in the fact that Bharatha would never come to fight.

Bharatha asked half the army to stay back and ordered the rest to follow him into the clearing where he could see a thatched cottage. There he saw Rama sitting with Sita, and Lakshmana. He was so overwhelmed by the sight of his beloved brothers and Sita that he ran forward and fell at Rama's feet, weeping with joy.

Rama lifted Bharatha, embraced him warmly and asked him if all was well. Bharatha could not bring himself to tell Rama about the sad demise of their father, but gathered the courage and said, "O Rama, our father could not live without you. He passed away six days after you left uttering your name even in his last breath. I have come to take you back to Ayodhya to crown you king according to father's wishes. Come with me and govern the people of Ayodhya who are without a king."

Hearing the news of his father's death, Rama was in deep pain as if an arrow had pierced his heart. He was shocked and Sita and Lakshmana, though in grief, consoled and comforted him. After a while, he rose, made his way towards the river Mandakini and offered prayers for his father's soul. He looked towards heaven and appealed to his father to provide direction and be a guiding light for him always.

As he returned to the hut, Sage Vashishta led the three Queens of King Dasharatha into the thatched cottage. They were shocked to see Rama, Sita and Lakshmana in the clothes of hermits and living in this simple a manner. Queen Kaushalya embraced Sita and said, "O daughter of Janaka, daughter-in-law of the great Dasharatha, my heart grieves at your plight. How can you live in a hut in the forest like this? Come back to the palace, O pride of Ayodhya!"

An assembly was held outside the cottage where Rama, Sita and Lakshmana had made their home in the forest. All the elders and Sages, Courtiers and Ministers stood with folded hands in front of Rama. Bharatha pleaded, "We have come to take you with us to the palace and crown you King of Ayodhya. The throne rightfully belongs to you. With your departure to the forest and the death of our father, the kingdom is plunged into gloom. Only you can disperse the darkness by taking over your rightful place on the throne as our King. So, I beg of you, please come back with us!"

Rama was overwhelmed by Bharatha's words but since he had given his father his word he could not go back on it. Rama replied to Bharatha, "My dear brother, you know that I cannot go against our father's last wish. If I fail to fulfil it, what kind of son would I be?"

He continued, "Go back to Ayodhya and rule as King. You have Shatrughna by your side. He will give you strength and courage. I have Lakshmana and Sita here with me. We will spend the fourteen years together and we will be safe. Have no fear. Everything will be alright."

Bharatha replied, "I have made up my mind. I will not rule Ayodhya. If you will not come back with me, then give me some belonging of yours to live by. At least, give me the sandals off your feet. I will place them on the throne and protect the kingdom in your name till your return from exile."

So, Rama handed over his sandals and blessed him with all his heart. Bharatha returned to Ayodhya with his sorrowful multitude, vowing to keep the kingdom safe for Rama and rule it justly on his behalf.

Rama In The Forest

After Bharatha's departure Rama, Sita and Lakshmana set off on their journey through the forest once again. The dense forest was dark and forbidding but the brave Princes and the beautiful Sita ventured on. Their life in the palace had not prepared them for such hardships, but they were the sons of a brave and legendary dynasty and their courage took them forward through many miles in the forest.

They admired the beauty of the forest, made friends with animals and trees alike and sat down to meals of fruits and herbs. Rama often said to Lakshmana that these experiences would prepare them for any other hardships later on in life. As they travelled through the forest, they decided to pay a visit to the noble sage Atri who lived in that part of the forest with his pious wife, Anusuya.

As they made their way towards the ashram, the beautiful flowers that grew all around the hermitage delighted them. Upon setting foot in the ashram, the Sage and his wife greeted them with great joy and thanked them for coming.

Rama explained to the Sage about why they were there and the Sage's wife took Sita under her care. With great affection Anusuya prepared a meal for the three guests while the Sage discussed the situation with Rama and Lakshmana.

The Sage and his wife also requested them to spend the night at the hermitage which they agreed to and resting their travel-weary limbs on beds of soft grass, fell into a restful sleep. In the morning, after a bath and prayers, they once again set off into the forest after receiving the Sage's blessings. The hermitage was soon behind them and the forest stretched ahead.

As they were travelling through the forest, they heard loud roars. Rama cautioned Lakshmana and Sita to be on guard. As the roars drew nearer, all the wild animals slunk away and the birds stopped chirping. The forest lay still and quiet.

All of a sudden a huge, man-eating demon, Viradha, broke through the dense trees and loomed upon them. He was known to stalk his prey in the forests, leaving none in peace and destroying everything in his wake. As soon as he saw the two Princes and the beautiful Sita, his eyes began to glow with an evil fire.

He decided that these three would make a good meal and laughed loudly and uproariously at his good fortune. He presumed that these humans would be no match to his demonic strength. Looking down at the three he decided to attend to Sita first as she would make a beautiful and delicate morsel.

He picked up Sita in his giant claws and got ready to eat her. Rama and Lakshmana immediately reacted and rained arrows upon him. The demon, distracted, put the Princess down and turned his attention to the two brothers. He decided that he would finish these two pests off first and then attend to the unprotected Princess.

He began to throw boulders at them. As the brothers rained one volley of arrows after the other, the demon fought fiercely. The piercing shafts of arrows had no effect on him. He hurled rocks and trees on them.

Rama then said to Lakshmana that as shooting arrows at him was having no effect, he had to be killed some other way. As the rain of arrows stopped, the demon was confused. Rama and Lakshmana immediately stt upon him and began to pommel him. This new strategy worked, the demon's strength slowly drained out, and Rama and Lakshmana thrashed him to death.

After slaying the evil Viradha, Rama and Lakshmana escorted Sita to a safe resting place. The three rested for a while and then decided to leave the place of evil as soon as possible. As they ventured further into the forest, they came to the hermitage of Sage Agastya.

The Sage received them with kind affection and welcomed them to his humble abode. The brothers fell at his feet and sought his blessings. The Sage embraced them and said, "It is I who am blessed by your presence here today. Do stay here in my humble abode and bless this part of the forest with your august presence."

Accepting his invitation to stay at his hermitage for the day, the two Princes and the Sage discussed many a thing, starting from their present condition to what they sought to achieve in the forest. Rama recounted the incidents of the many demons they had met and slain on their journey through the forest.

Rama also said, "I would like to rid the forest of all the demons and rakshasas and make it habitable for good folks. I have my brave brother Lakshmana to protect me and my pious wife Sita to give me courage."

Said the Sage to Rama, "If you would like to rid the forest of all the demons, you must take up residence at Panchavati. Build an abode there and live with your brother and wife. It is a peaceful place and you will be able to fulfil your mission from there."

The Sage then gave Rama several divine weapons and taught him the mantras to use them. The two brothers and Sita took leave of the Sage after seeking his blessings. He wished them well and also prayed for their success. The three then set off towards Panchavati, which was now to be their abode.

As they made their way to Panchavati, they met many a Sage. They sought each ones blessings and prayers for their well-being. Soon they reached Panchavati and were completely smitten by the beauty of the place. It was abundantly green, with many a lush stream running by and it was home to the gentlest of animals and birds. The trees grew tall and the plants bore beautiful flowers in many a hue.

Lakshmana offered to build a hut for the three of them. Rama was pleased at his offer and shed tears of joy at his brother's devotion. He blessed Lakshmana and proclaimed, "You and I will be inseparable forever."

Lakshmana made walls of mud, which he kneaded with his affection for Rama and Sita. He then built the frame of the roof, which he tied with his devotion for his brother. Finally he put the thatch in and blessed it with his loyalty to Rama and Sita. The abode for the Princes of Ayodhya and the daughter of Janaka was now ready!

Panchavati prospered under the scions of the Raghu dynasty. They enjoyed its beauty. Its peaceful and calm atmosphere healed the pain of the many hardships that they had already been through. The Sages living around this peaceful place, made the experience richer by offering advice and blessings. The gentle animals befriended them and roamed in their gardens, under the loving care of Sita.

Sita found peace in Panchavati. The daughter of Janaka who had been through so much hardship already, finally found the happiness she desired. She lived happily with her husband and his loving and devoted brother, who served them lovingly. They grew flowers and herbs and vegetables and decorated their humble abode. Happiness and bliss was finally theirs.

Shoorpanakha Visits Panchavati

The serene surroundings, the beautiful place, the company of Sages, the gentle animals and the fresh food at Panchvati, all served to make their stay in the forest happy and comfortable. The golden days passed slowly. One day after their bath in the Godavari and prayers, Rama and Sita were admiring the beauty around them while the devoted Lakshmana was attending to some chores.

Shoorpanakha, the sister of the mighty demon king Ravana, was passing through the forest. As she neared the thatched abode at Panchavati, she stopped. She was taken in by the peace and beauty of the place. She saw a handsome man and a beautiful woman sitting in front of a beautiful cottage. She saw another handsome man attending to some chores. As she took everything in, her gaze stopped at Rama. She could not take her eyes off him and was completely smitten by the handsome good looks of the Raghu Prince.

Shoorpanakha was a very ugly demoness. However, with her magical powers she could assume any form at will. She knew that in order to attract the handsome man, she would need to be very beautiful. So, she transformed herself into a lovely maiden, with fair skin and beautiful features. Her hair turned long and silky and her limbs became graceful and slim. Her rough garb turned into beautiful clothes of the richest silk and her thick demon jewellery transformed into the finest pieces of jewellery, rich with gems.

She wound flowers into her hair and slowly emerged from her hiding place in the shrubs and bushes. She looked very beautiful. Her face shone like the sun and her long hair glittered in the light. Walking gracefully, she shyly approached Rama and said, "O handsome man! I have fallen in love with you. I have already taken you for my husband. I will die if you do not marry me." So saying, she fell at Rama's feet.

Rama turned to her and said, "O fair maiden! Rise! Beautiful as you are, I cannot marry you. I am already married and this is my beautiful and virtuous wife Sita! We are very happy together." Shoorpanakha was very disappointed, but the cunning demoness that she was, she immediately turned her attention to Lakshmana. His fair skin and strong looks appealed to her. She went up to him and said shyly, "What about you? Why don't you marry me? We are so good looking and you are also strong. We will make a good couple. Our children will be the most beautiful in the land."

Lakshmana said to her, "I am but a slave of my brother Rama, and you look like a princess. How can I marry you? It would not befit a princess like you to take a slave like me for a husband." Shoorpanakha was enraged. Both the brothers had tactfully turned her down. This irked her. After all, wasn't she beautiful? So, what was stopping either of these two handsome men from taking her as his wife?

Her gaze fell on Sita. So this human creature was the obstacle that was keeping the two men from marrying her! It was her beauty they were smitten by. If this lady was removed she could marry either of these handsome men. She turned to Sita and screamed, "You are the one who is keeping these two handsome men away from me. If I get rid of you, then I can have any of them."

She sprang upon Sita saying, "I will devour you, you fiend! You will no longer stand between me and these handsome men, whom I have fallen in love with." All of a sudden the grace and the beauty of the lovely maiden was gone and the rough ways of the demoness came to the fore. She pounced on the gentle Sita. Sita was totally unprepared for such an attack and cowered under the strength of the evil Shoorpanakha!

Rama immediately came to Sita's rescue and fended Shoorpanakha off just in time. He told her to stay away from Sita and should only speak to him or his brother. She should keep Sita out of this. When Shoorpanakha refused to see reason, Rama asked Lakshmana to attend to her.

Lakshmana ordered Shoorpanakha to leave their abode and not come back again. He told her that neither he nor his brother was interested in marrying her and that she should leave them alone.

Said Shoorpanakha to Lakshmana, "You do not know who I am, or you would not speak to me like this. When you realise who I am, you will beg at my feet, you mortal. You will beg me for your life and then I will devour not only you and your brother, but also this wretched woman who keeps me away from the two of you."

So saying, the wicked demoness assumed her true form. Her limbs became rough and her rich clothes fell away to reveal her rough demon clothes. Her skin became dark and her hair turned rough. Her nails grew back like claws and her jewellery changed back. Now she once again was Shoorpanakha, the demoness.

Her grace vanished and she assumed her enormous strength. She fought fiercely and hard and it took all of Lakshmana's strength to keep her at bay. Lakshmana was a courageous warrior, who had been trained by skillful gurus. He fought cleverly and Shoorpanakha could not harm him. Every move that she made, Lakshmana had a countermove.

Finally, Lakshmana lunged at her and with a great sweep of his sword, chopped her nose off. The nose fell, bleeding to the ground. Shoorpanakha screamed and shouted curses at Lakshmana.

So humiliated was she that she vowed revenge on the two brothers. She said, "I will bring back all the demon armies to destroy you. There will be no trace left of the three of you after my brothers have finished with you." So saying, she ran off into the forest.

She reached the mountain abode of her two brothers Khara and Dushana. The two demons lived in caves in the mountains. They were aghast at the sight of their sister mutilated and bleeding. Shoorpanakha screamed, "What use is your strength if somebody can humiliate your own sister? See what Rama and Lakshmana have done to me! Go out and destroy them to avenge this humiliation and prove yourself to be men of valour."

Khara and Dushana asked her to recount the entire tale. When they heard of her humiliation at the hands of Rama and Lakshmana, they vowed to kill the two brothers.

With fourteen thousand demon soldiers in tow, Khara and Dushana set off to attack Rama and Lakshmana. As they saw the army approaching, Rama and Lakshmana took up their bows and arrows and faced the demon army. Firing volley after volley of arrows into the army, Rama proved his skills. Demon soldiers fell in hundreds and thousands. Elephants, horses, chariots all fell as the shower of arrows continued. Rama also used his cosmic powers. He turned all the demon soldiers into his image. The demons saw one another in the form of Rama, so they fought among themselves and perished along with Khara and Dushana.

There was not a single demon left standing. Emerging victorious the brothers surveyed the destruction they had wrought. The Devas, on witnessing this, showered flowers and blessings from the heavens.

The Golden Deer

When Rama destroyed the army of fourteen thousand demon soldiers, Akampana was the only survivor. He fled the battlefield and made his way to Lanka, where on the throne sat the King of Demons, Ravana, the mighty warrior with ten heads and the power of ten thousand.

Ravana was enraged when he learnt that his brothers, the mighty Khara and Dushana had been killed in battle and their army of fourteen thousand demon soldiers completely destroyed. He bellowed in rage, "Who is it who dared to face my army and kill my demon brothers?" Akampana cowered in fear and said, "It was Rama, the Prince of Ayodhya. He killed your brave brothers single-handedly and annihilated your army." He further added that there was no way anybody could harm Rama. The only way to hurt him would be through his beloved and beautiful wife, Sita. Akampana suggested, "Kidnap Sita, O Ravana. That will bring Rama to his knees."

Ravana's lust for the beautiful Sita was aroused by Akampana. Thinking about Sita's divine beauty, that Akampana had praised and marvelled at, he hatched an evil plan. He approached Mareecha, the son of Tadaka, the dreadful demoness. Mareecha had given up his evil ways and was leading the life of an ascetic in the forest.

Said Ravana to Mareecha, "Rama, Prince of Ayodhya, attacked my demon brothers, Khara and Dushana, and completely routed my army of fourteen thousand demon soldiers, single-handedly. I am told that he is invincible. I want to kidnap his beautiful wife Sita and teach him a lesson. I need your help."

Mareecha advised Ravana against this dastardly act. He said, "Rama is all powerful. Your desire to kidnap his wife is to ask for the destruction of the entire demon race. Go back to your magnificent palace, enjoy the riches of your kingdom with your beautiful wives, forget Sita and leave the mighty Rama alone." Ravana bowed to Mareecha's sane advice and returned to Lanka.

After Ravana returned to his prosperous island kingdom, the evil Shoorpanakha followed him there, running and screaming, bleeding and mutilated. Her evil face shone with hatred and she provoked him, "Are you so well-settled in your own wealth and in the company of your beautiful wives, that you do not see how your sister has been insulted and hurt? Rama's brother Lakshmana did this to me, as I struggled to carry off Sita."

Ravana was agitated once again. He sent Shoorpanakha away, promising to avenge her insult. He then thought about Rama and the beautiful Sita, his dead brothers and his destroyed army. He also thought about what Mareecha had said. The more he brooded, his rage became greater. He finally decided to kidnap the beautiful Sita, to avenge the death of his brothers and the insult meted out to his sister. Reports of Sita's beauty also excited him. He decided that by kidnaping her, he would kill two birds with one stone - have her for himself and also seek revenge.

Ravana set his evil plan in motion. He visited Mareecha again. This time he did not seek advice. He used all his cunning tactics to lure Mareecha into his evil plan. Said Ravana, "Mareecha, I must avenge what has happened to Shoorpanakha. Her mutilation and humiliation cannot be ignored. To teach the brothers from Ayodhya a lesson, I plan to carry Sita away from Panchavati and I need the help of your cunning and magical powers to do so."

Mareecha wanted to refuse but Ravana warned him, "I will behead you right now if you do not help me. This is no longer a request, it is a command." Frightened and trembling, Mareecha said, "What do I have to do?"

Ravana smiled wickedly and outlined his plan. "I want you to assume the form of a golden deer. Go to where Rama and Sita live and attract Sita's attention. She will ask Rama to hunt the deer for her. When he is away, I will abduct her."

Left with no choice, Mareecha had to do what Ravana commanded. He flew to the Dandaka forests with Ravana and reached the beautiful abode of Rama at Panchavati. Mareecha then assumed the form of a beautiful golden deer with luminous spots that shimmered like silver in the sunlight, while Ravana watched, hidden behind the dense foliage in the forest.

As the golden deer grazed, it slowly approached the hut, where the brothers and Sita were resting. At the sight of this wonderful animal, Sita was delighted and spell-bound. Its beauty attracted her and its grace bewitched her so much that she wanted the deer for herself. She entreated with Rama, "Look, what a wonderful creature! Its skin shines like gold and there are a thousand gems on it! Do capture the beautiful deer for me, my Lord." Rama picked up his bow and said, "I will go after it, my dearest." He instructed Lakshmana to look after Sita and asked him not to leave her side, come what may.

As Rama ran after the deer, it gamboled away and led him further and further away from the hut. Rama chased the deer and finally let an arrow fly from his bow. The arrow caught the beast in its heart. As it was dying, the beast resumed its natural form of Mareecha who with his magical powers cried out in his dying breath, "Oh Sita! Oh Lakshmana!" in the voice of Rama.

The voice rang through the forest and reached the anxious ears of Sita and Lakshmana. Sita's heart almost stopped and she asked Lakshmana to go to the rescue of Rama. Lakshmana who had been instructed by his elder brother to stay put by Sita's side, come what may, hesitated to leave her. However, Sita commanded him to go as she felt that Rama's life was in danger. Lakshmana paused for a moment, then invoked a prayer and bending down drew a line with his arrow around the hut. He requested Sita not to cross it and also added that nobody would be able to come across the line and harm her. The evil Ravana was watching from his hiding spot. As soon as Lakshmana sped away in the direction of Rama's voice, Ravana put the second part of his plan into action.

He donned the robes of a hermit and approached the hut. He chanted hymns and bent his head in prayer as he neared the door of the hut. On hearing a voice, Sita came out. Ravana was truly amazed by her extraordinary beauty. Both Akampana and Shoorpanakha had done no justice to Sita in describing her beauty. She was a great deal lovelier than all his wives put together. Her beauty glowed and goodness shone on her face. Even without her royal garments and bejewelled only with a few jewels and the flowers of the forest, Sita was quite a sight!

The hermit asked her for alms. She went inside the hut and brought them for him. Standing on her side of the line she offered him the fruits. The hermit asked her to come out. When she refused, he pretended to be offended. "Do you not trust me?" he asked, "I am a man of God!" The innocent Sita, not sensing any danger, stepped across Lakshmana's line and offered the hermit alms. The hermit roared with evil laughter and revealed his true form, the King of Demons, the King of Lanka, Ravana! He caught hold of Sita's hair and summoned his flying chariot. He threw her in and flew away, towards his kingdom in the far South.

Meanwhile, Lakshmana found Rama retracing his steps. He was happy to see his brother safe, but alarmed when he thought of the dying voice that had called out to him. He ran up to Rama, and said, "You are safe!" Rama replied, "I am safe, but why did you leave Sita alone? I hope she is safe. Why did you come away? Did I not tell you to stay by her side, come what may?" When Lakshmana explained, Rama cried, "The voice you heard was that of the deer, which turned into a demon when it died. Oh! I hope this is not part of an evil plan."

The brothers ran to their hut, but Rama's worst fears came true. The hut was empty; a salver of fruits lay scattered outside the door and there was no sign of Sita. The Prince of Ayodhya had lost his beautiful, virtuous wife. Rama was devastated and sat there, his head in his hands. Then he rose and said to Lakshmana, "We must find Sita. There are evil forces we ought to conquer. I will need your help and support." So saying, Rama, the righteous, led his brother Lakshmana into the forest, in search of his wife, the peerless princess, Sita.

Rama Meets Hanuman

Rama and Lakshmana on returning to the hermitage at Panchvati were grief-stricken on finding that Sita was missing. Rama was in total despair as to what misfortune may have befallen her. He asked the plants and trees and the animals all around if they had seen Sita or known anything that may have happened. The trees shrank and the animals hung their heads in sorrow. Lakshmana tried to console him as best as he could. Finally, Rama said, "We must look for her, even if it means going to the ends of the earth!"

They set off looking for Sita. After an agonisingly long walk, they came upon Jatayu, the vulture, who was lying mortally wounded on the ground. As Rama picked up the wounded bird, it said to him, gasping for breath, "O Rama! Ravana, the demon-king of Lanka has carried off your beloved Sita. I tried to stop him as he was racing across the skies, but he cut off my wings. I have clung to life to tell you this. Now my mission is accomplished." So saying, the noble bird breathed its last.

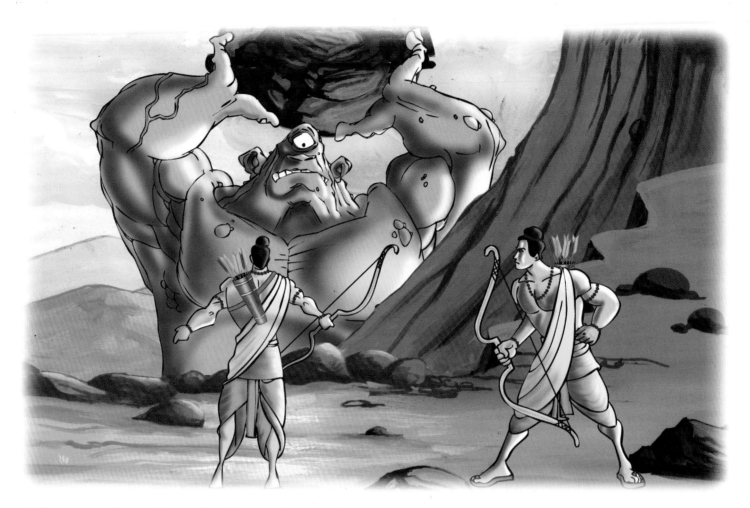

After performing the last rites of Jatayu, Rama and Lakshmana moved on. They hoped in their hearts that Sita would come to no harm at the hands of the demon-king, Ravana. They moved on looking for signs of Sita, which would give them a clue as to where she had been taken. As they headed south towards Lanka, a huge roar greeted them and a one-eyed demon came into sight. This was Kabandha, huge as a giant and his head seemed to touch the clouds. He looked hideous because he had just one eye. He picked up a huge rock and threw it at the Raghu brothers.

They dodged the rock, but the one-eyed monster picked them up in the twinkling of an eye. However, Rama and Lakshmana quickly unsheathed their swords, cut off the monster's arms and killed him. The two brothers then burnt his body. As his body turned into ashes, a beautiful Gandharva emerged. He thanked Rama for delivering him from a curse. "I am now free from the curse. If you wish to find Sita, befriend the King of the Vanaras, Sugreeva." So saying, he rose to the heavens.

Upon Kabandha's advice, Rama and Lakshmana set off looking for Sugreeva, the King of the Vanaras and reached the banks of the river Pampa. On the banks of the river lived Sabhari, an old woman, who was a disciple of the famous Sage Matanga. Her guru had told her that she would be blessed with a visit by Rama, the incarnation of Lord Vishnu. When Rama and Lakshmana reached her hermitage, she knew at once that they were the ones she had been waiting for and rushed to receive them. She felt blessed indeed.

She fed them with the best fruits from the forest. In fact, to ensure that the fruits that Rama ate were sweet, she tasted them before she offered them to him. Rama was touched by her innocence and devotion. He said to Sabhari, "You are truly blessed! I am amazed at the extent of your devotion. I grant you the abode of eternal bliss!" As soon as he said this, the fire of Yoga consumed the old woman and she merged with the supreme being in eternal bliss. Rama and Lakshmana then resumed their quest for Sugreeva.

As they were walking through the forest, looking for Sita, Rama's heart was very heavy. He thought of how his beloved has had to face many hardships after becoming his consort. He said to Lakshmana, "I love her so much. Maybe this is the test of my love. Even though I am full of grief we must be brave and find her." Lakshmana gave his brother all the encouragement he could.

Meanwhile Sugreeva, the King of the Vanaras, spotted the two Raghu brothers coming towards him and was alarmed. He thought that they had been sent by his brother Vaali to kill him. He sent Hanuman, the son of Vayu, saying, "Go and see who they are and what they want." Hanuman disguised himself as a brahmin and approached the two brothers. He said, "Who are you, kind Lords and what brings you to this part of the forest?" Rama replied, "We are the sons of Dasharatha of Ayodhya and are in the forest at our father's command. We are now looking for my wife Sita, the virtuous daughter of King Janaka of Mithila who has been kidnapped by a demon called Ravana."

As soon as Hanuman realised that these were Rama and Lakshmana, he fell at Rama's feet to seek his blessings. He had been waiting for his Lord to appear before him and now his prayers had been answered! Rama blessed him and asked him to rise.

Hanuman revealed himself to his Lord in his true form, that of a monkey. "I am Hanuman," he said. "I have been waiting for you, my Lord!" Rama was deeply touched by his devotion and said, "Can you help us, O son of Vayu?" Hanuman replied, "I will take you to Sugreeva, the King of the Vanaras who has a large army at his command. He will surely help you. Right now, he lives in the forest because his brother Vaali has usurped his kingdom. I am sure you can also help him to regain his kingdom !"

Rama was delighted, "O Hanuman! We have been looking for Sugreeva and now he has sent you to us! Truly this is the work of one who is supreme and divine! Lead us to Sugreeva and let us see what good we can do for each other!"

Hanuman made himself larger with his supernatural powers and beckoned Rama and Lakshmana, "Get on my shoulders as the way through the forest is treacherous and you will find it difficult to reach Sugreeva. I will fly you both there. It will be much easier and I will also have the honour of serving you!"

Rama and Lakshmana got on his shoulders and they took off. Rama was amazed by Hanuman's strength. Hanuman flew above the trees in the forest and Rama and Lakshmana could see for miles all around them. As soon as Sugreeva saw Hanuman flying towards his abode with two men on his shoulders he knew that they were friends and prepared to welcome them.

As Hanuman landed and set the two brothers on the ground, a loud cheer went up from the monkeys gathered on the Rishyamukh mountain. Hanuman then went across to Sugreeva's abode and announced the arrival of the Raghu brothers.

Hanuman said to Sugreeva, "O King of the Vanaras, these men are none other than the Raghu Princes, Rama and Lakshmana. They are looking for Rama's divine consort, Sita, who has been carried away by the demon-king Ravana. They need your help to look for her! Help them and Rama, the divine, will surely help you get back your kingdom from your brother Vaali!"

As soon as Sugreeva heard Hanuman's account, he rushed out to greet the two brothers. He embraced Rama and said, "Blessed am I, that I can help you in your hour of need! My army of monkeys, strong and alert, is at your command. They will find Sita and help you get her back. It will be their duty!"

Rama was overjoyed to hear this. He embraced Sugreeva warmly and said, "I am grateful to you, O Sugreeva, the King of the Vanaras. I have been looking for you and now I am sure that Sita will be back with me, very soon!"

Sugreeva then led Rama to his abode in the forest. After having made the two brothers comfortable, Sugreeva asked his monkey subjects if they knew the whereabouts of Sita. The monkeys replied that they had indeed witnessed a demon in a flying chariot, taking a beautiful lady away with him. She had been tearful and had thrown down her ornaments, as they flew past which they had picked up and kept safe. Rama said, "Show them to me." When he saw Sita's ornaments, he broke down, "Indeed they are hers! The vile fiend has taken her away!"

Sugreeva consoled him and said, "Do not grieve, O Rama! We will surely find her!" "Yes! We must! I cannot bear to see her in Ravana's custody. She is my Sita and I will get her back!" So saying, he forged his friendship with Sugreeva and the two men decided they would spare no efforts in rescuing Sita from the demon-king Ravana!

Rama Slays Vaali

After it was decided that Sugreeva's army would be at Rama's disposal and that they would together endeavour to find and bring Sita back, Sugreeva began to tell Rama about the sorry state of his own affairs. He narrated how his brother Vaali, had usurped his kingdom and driven him away.

Sugreeva had to live in the Rishyamukh hills which were out of bounds for Vaali because of the curse on him of a sage whom he had annoyed, while Vaali lived in the palace of the King of the Vanaras. Sugreeva also added that Vaali was much stronger and therefore difficult to defeat and that he had also taken Sugreeva's wife as his own. Sugreeva said "Unless I defeat him in a one-to-one combat, I will not be able to regain my kingdom and my people. You will have to help me." Rama assured him he would.

Rama said to Sugreeva, "Challenge Vaali to a one-to-one fight. Tell him that the winner shall be the King of Kishkindha, the kingdom of the Vanaras." Rama, Lakshmana, Sugreeva and Hanuman set off for Kishkindha. Sugreeva challenged Vaali to a contest of strength and skill. Rama stood away from the clearing, hiding behind some bushes. Sugreeva and Vaali began to fight fiercely. The birds and the beasts grew silent as the two monkey Kings fought each other.

Rama took aim to kill Vaali, but was bewildered. The two brothers looked very alike and as they fought their forms and features appeared very similar. Their method of fighting was also the same and Rama was not able to differentiate one from the other. His confusion grew as he took aim repeatedly. He decided to stay put and bide his time. Meanwhile, Sugreeva became tired and weak as he was grievously wounded by Vaali. He had to flee the scene of battle and return to his abode in the Rishyamukh mountains.

Later as Rama and Sugreeva took stock in the latters abode Rama said, "I will need something to differentiate you from Vaali. Not only do you look alike, you also fight in the same manner. For fear of hurting you, I couldn't shoot my arrows. Wear this garland and fight again and this time, I will surely slay him."

So Sugreeva wore the garland and went back to Kishkindha and yet again challenged Vaali from the gates of the monkey palace. Vaali came out of the palace, roaring in anger. The battle was fiercer this time. The earth moved as the two Kings pitted their strength against each other. Vaali was stronger but Sugreeva had Rama by his side. When Rama, who was hiding behind some bushes, saw that Sugreeva was tiring, he let loose an arrow from his bow. The arrow pierced Vaali's heart and he fell with a loud crash. Before breathing his last, Vaali entrusted his wife and children to Sugreeva's care and sought mercy for his sins. Sugreeva promised to take care of his loved ones.

With the death of Vaali, Sugreeva was crowned King and Vaali's son, Angada, was made crown prince. The celebrations of the coronation continued for days. Sugreeva was so happy to get his kingdom back and to be living in the palace that his promise to Rama soon slipped from his mind. Rama and Lakshmana lived in the caves in the Rishyamukh waiting for Sugreeva to do his bit.

Hanuman decided to take matters into his own hands and went to Sugreeva to remind him of his promise. Sugreeva realised his mistake and ordered his vast army to collect at the Rishyamukh. He went to Rama and Lakshmana and said, "My army is at your command. Shall I send them out to look for Sita first?" On Rama's approval, Sugreeva commanded the monkeys to spread in every direction and look for Sita. Rama gave Hanuman his ring, to prove to Sita that he was Rama's messenger. With hope in his heart he wished all of them luck and hoped that they would come back with some good news as fast as possible.

As soon as the order was given, the army split into four and decided to go in all four directions, looking for Sita, Rama's divine consort. They were also joined by the bear army commandeered by Jambavan. Hanuman, Angada and Jambavan were part of one group and decided to head South looking for Sita. The other three groups went North, East and West. A month passed and Rama was getting anxious. The three groups that went North, East and West, made their way back to Kishkindha and reported that they had not found any trace of Sita. Rama was disheartened, but Lakshmana consoled him and said, "Hanuman and his party are not back yet. Be patient and I am sure, he will bring good news."

Meanwhile, Hanuman and his men had passed many a wild terrain and met an ascetic, Swayamprabha who helped the monkeys refresh themselves. When she learned of their mission, she was keen to help those who were helping the divine Rama. With the use of her ascetic powers she, in the wink of an eye, transported the entire group to the tip of South India.

As the monkeys and bears reached the shore and looked towards the vast ocean, they saw the powerful waves strongly breaking over the shore. They were confused and were trying to figure out what to do next. Meanwhile, Sampati, the King of vultures saw the huge army of monkeys and bears and thought to himself that a big feast was in store for him. He was famished for a long time and flew towards the army. As he approached them, he overheard the monkeys talking about how Jatayu, his brother, had died trying to save Sita from Ravana. Sampati, far from being hungry now, was in fact saddened to hear of his brother's death, but was proud that he had died trying to save Sita.

Wanting to help them, Sampati told the monkeys and bears, "With my keen sight, I can see her across the ocean. She is held captive by Ravana in Lanka and many demonesses guard her." The monkeys were happy to hear that Sita had been located. They knew that if they could cross the ocean, they could reach her, but how would they manage to cross the mighty ocean?

As they were pondering over this, Jambavan, the leader of the bears had an idea. He said, "The one among us who can jump the farthest is the one who is most likely to reach Lanka." Gaja, the young brave monkey could jump ten yojanas, Gavaksha could jump twenty, a third monkey warrior said that he could jump thirty… Jambavan himself could jump ninety yojanas, but Lanka was a hundred yojanas away. Angada, the crown prince said that he could jump a hundred yojanas, but he would not be able to return, as the first jump would take away all his strength.

Meanwhile Hanuman, the son of Vayu, was silent. Jambavan looked at him and said, "You are the one who can do it, Hanuman. Remember once as a small boy, you had jumped into the sky, trying to get to the sun, because you thought it was a fruit meant to be eaten? You are truly blessed by Brahma and Indra. You are immortal and imperishable, O Hanuman, and only you can jump across the sea to Lanka!"

Hanuman was inspired by Jambavan's words who further said, "Think of Rama's purpose and his mission, think of his grief and sorrow over losing Sita. Only you can give him back his happiness. It is all in your hands. Rise, O great one and leap across the sea. Bring word from Sita and gladden Rama's heart."

Hanuman rose and with one mighty intake of breath, he began to grow in size. The monkeys and bears cheered him on. There was a divine light that glowed around his body. He was the true servant of the Lord and now it was his turn to do his bidding. Soon he was as tall as a mountain and turned to face Lanka. The monkeys and the bears wished him luck. Hanuman knew he should get across to Lanka and see that Sita was well, though that would not be enough. He would also have to bring back word from her for his Lord, Rama. That was his mission and succeed he would!

ᵔ Hanuman Goes To Lanka ᵔ

As Hanuman stood at the seashore, his form as big as a mountain, he could see Lanka across the ocean. It was but an island and he knew he could jump across the mighty ocean and reach it. With the good wishes of the monkeys and bears ringing in his ears, Hanuman took a deep breath and leaped into the sky. There was a roar from the monkeys and bears below as they were delighted to see the son of the wind-god Vayu, take to the air towards Lanka.

As he flew towards Lanka, with the giant ocean spread out under him, he was completely focused on his task and his sights were set on the island far away. While he was flying, a giant mountain, Mynaka, rose from the seas and said, "Rest awhile, Hanuman and then continue with your journey!" Hanuman struck the mountain with his mighty chest and said, "There is no rest for me till my mission is accomplished. Move out of my way!" So saying, he flew on.

The air roared as Hanuman sped through the sky. His giant shadow fell upon the ocean like a ship. Seeing his shadow, a demoness called Surasa rose from under the waters and stopped Hanuman midway through his flight. "Where do you think you are going, you monkey?" she bellowed. "Let me pass," said Hanuman. "I will let you go if you can fly through my mouth, or else I will eat you up," said Surasa and started growing in size with her mouth becoming bigger and bigger.

Hanuman grew too. He made himself more bigger, but Surasa was a demoness so the bigger Hanuman became, the bigger she made her mouth. Finally, her mouth looked like a cavern that could take in many a mountain. Then intelligently, in the twinkling of an eye, Hanuman made himself as small as a fly and flew in and out of the great cavernous mouth of Surasa. Surasa was impressed and so she blessed him, "Go, brave Hanuman, and accomplish your mission," she said. "You are truly a brave warrior and are matchless in your physical and intellectual prowess. Besides, you also have the strength of purpose!"

Hanuman had to face many a demon and demoness on his way to Lanka. He overcame all of them and finally sighted the shores of Lanka. The land was like a green jewel in the blue ocean. Covered with plantain and coconut trees, Lanka looked peaceful and inviting. Hanuman landed on a mountain in Lanka to better understand the geography of the place. He could see the entire island from his perch. The land was rich and there was wealth everywhere. There was more wealth in Lanka than in Indra's and Kubera's kingdoms put together.

Hanuman looked around. The rich palaces were covered with gold. The people wore rich clothes and the streets were full of beautiful men and women, wearing large amounts of precious jewellery. Everywhere he looked there were lush gardens. Hanuman took all of this in and thought over what he should do next. He had to find Sita first, so he planned that he would let darkness fall and thereafter venture into Lanka.

Slowly the sun set over the rich land and Hanuman waited until it was dark. He then made himself as small as a normal monkey so that he could move around unnoticed and enter Lanka which was heavily guarded. Hanuman looked through all the rich palaces and the beautiful mansions but Sita was nowhere to be found. He travelled from one palace to another. There were beautiful women sleeping in all the palaces but Hanuman knew that none of them could be Sita. He even went into Ravana's palace and saw him lying there, as large as a mountain, on a golden bed studded with precious stones and diamonds. Ravana's huge form made Hanuman tremble. He looked around for Sita but she was not to be found there either.

Where would he find the Lord's divine consort? Then he realised that Sita would never be in any of the rich palaces. He went out and came upon a garden by the side of a temple. Hanuman jumped into the garden and looked around. There, under a tree sat a divinely beautiful woman. Hanuman instantly knew that he had found Lord Rama's Sita!

Sita sat in the Ashoka Garden surrounded by many demonesses and looking very unhappy. She also looked pale and Hanuman could see that she had been crying. The demonesses surrounding her spoke to her of Ravana's might and power. "Marry him," they said, "He is more powerful than any other on earth. He will make you very happy!" Sita replied, "There is none as powerful as my Lord Rama!"

Suddenly, there was a huge roar as Ravana came to the Ashoka Garden, accompanied by many a soldier and guard. He roared at Sita, "I have begged and pleaded with you. What more do you want? Why won't you marry me? Don't you see how rich and powerful I will make you?" Sita plucked a blade of grass and threw it at Ravana, "O evil one! Your power and wealth are like this blade of grass which my Lord Rama will crush beneath his feet. You are nothing but a thief. I will never be yours!" Dejected and crest-fallen, Ravana went away. The soldiers, guards and demonesses also left. Sita was now alone in the garden.

Hanuman had witnessed the entire scene. As soon as he saw everybody leave, he began to sing praises of Lord Rama from his perch on the tree. Sita was overjoyed to hear her Lord's name being mentioned over and over again. She asked the singer to come down and reveal himself. Hanuman jumped down from his perch and bowed at Sita's feet.

"Who are you? And why do you sing praises of my Lord Rama?" said Sita. Hanuman replied, "O Mother, I am Hanuman, the messenger from your Lord Rama. He has given me this ring to give to you." So saying, he handed over Rama's ring to Sita.

As soon as Sita saw the ring she was overjoyed and here eyes welled with tears of joy. "Grieve no more, Mother! Very soon Rama and Lakshmana will come to Lanka with a huge army of monkeys and bears, vanquish Ravana and take you back." Sita's joy knew no bounds. Finally, her prayers had been answered.

After reassuring Sita, Hanuman thought about his next course of action. He knew he had to meet Ravana and warn him of the destruction that the abduction of Sita was sure to bring him. Before he set about attracting the attention of the guards and demonesses he bowed at Sita's feet and received her blessings.

He noisily jumped on to the trees, and began to eat the fruit throwing down what he did not devour. Then he plucked leaves from the trees and strew them all over the garden. As he saw the guards and demonesses nearing him, he began uprooting the trees and fought them with all his might. When they found that they could not control him, the guards ran to Ravana and said, "There is a monkey who is destroying the Ashoka Garden, O Lord!" Ravana was enraged. How dare a mere monkey destroy his most beautiful garden? He sent out a large army of demons and demonesses led by his beloved son Aksha, to capture the monkey.

When Hanuman saw the large army approaching him, he uprooted a large tree and wrought havoc, killing many a demon and demoness. Aksha was also killed, crushed by the rain of trees that were thrown at him. The rest of the army took to its heels and ran back to Ravana. Hearing of his beloved son's death, Ravana ordered his most powerful son, Indrajit, to destroy the monkey.

Indrajit mounted his chariot and rode to capture the monkey. Hanuman fought bravely and defeated Indrajit's every move. Finally Indrajit, or Meghnath as he was also called, used the Brahmastra, a divine arrow, on Hanuman. Under the might of the Brahmastra, Hanuman fell. The demon soldiers then tied up Hanuman and Indrajit dragged him away to Ravana's court. Hanuman knew that the Brahmastra could only keep him down for less than an hour and since he wanted to meet Ravana to deliver Lord Rama's message the mighty Hanuman let himself be dragged away. His mission was progressing well!

❧ Lanka On Fire ❧

Hanuman was presented before Ravana, who sat on a throne of gold draped with golden silk that was exquisitely decorated with pearls, gems and precious stones. Ravana's lust for gold was insatiable and known to all. Hanuman was not offered a seat, so he stood a while and then made his tail long, coiled it into a seat and sat high up at an imposing height. Ravana asked Hanuman, "Who has sent you? Is it Indra or Kubera?"

Hanuman replied politely, "I have not been sent by Indra or Kubera. I am a messenger of Lord Rama and am the Chief Minister of the great Sugreeva, King of the Vanaras. It was cowardice on your part to abduct Princess Sita. Send her back at once to Lord Rama with all due respect and seek refuge at Lord Rama's feet. I warn you O, demon King, if you fail to do this immediately, all the boons you have acquired shall fail you and your entire demon race will be destroyed." Ravana roared with laughter, scoffing at Hanuman's words.

Hearing Hanuman's preachings and warnings Ravana lost his temper, rose to his feet and bellowed, "You impudent monkey, don't you realise that you are speaking to the mightiest king of all asuras? I can snatch away your life in a moment. You dare to insult me in my own court!" Turning to his soldiers he shouted, "Kill this impudent monkey at once." His soldiers and courtiers rushed to do his bidding but they were stopped by Vibheeshana, Ravana's brother. He spoke in a low voice to Ravana, "O great King of Kings. It is not right to kill a messenger. After all, a messenger is one who carries only a message. It is not his fault that the message does not please you."

Ravana always listened to his brother's advice because he knew that he would only speak the truth. He then ordered his soldiers to set Hanuman's tail on fire. The soldiers took hold of Hanuman's tail and started to cover it with rags of cloth. But Hanuman kept elongating his tail to make the task more difficult. Finally they covered all of it, dipped it in oil and set it on fire.

Hanuman was then paraded through the streets of Lanka and the people who had gathered, mocked him and said, "Look! There goes the thief who entered our city." Meanwhile Sita heard of Hanuman's plight and felt very sad. She at once kindled a fire and started praying to Agni, the god of fire, "O Agni! Please save him. Let Hanuman be immune to your flames."

As Hanuman was being led around the city, he decided to teach everyone a lesson. Shrinking himself in size, he shook off the ropes that bound him. Then, in an instant, he made himself as tall as a mountain and jumped onto a tall building setting it on fire. Jumping from house to house he set everything in his path on fire.

The wind fanned the flames and soon the whole city of Lanka was enveloped in a blazing fire. Tall turrets of smoke billowed out and reached for the skies. Hanuman continued his fiery assault on the golden city of Lanka, till the whole city burned in a golden glow.

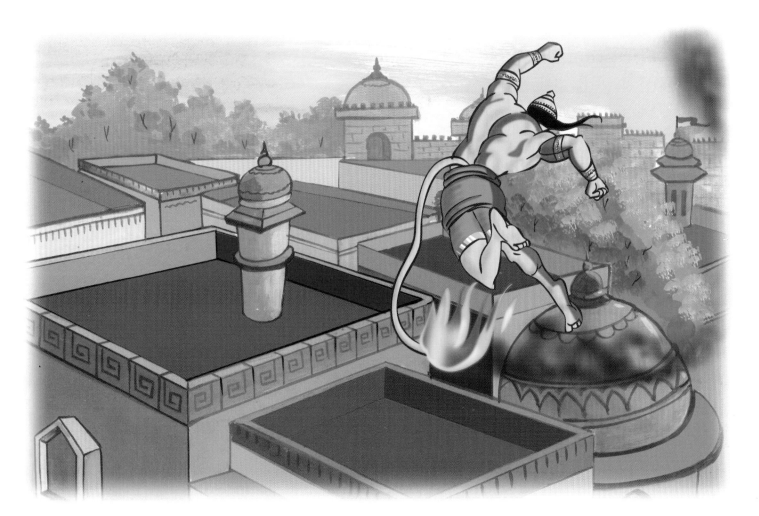

The swift attack on Lanka reduced the city of wealth and riches to ashes. The green and gold city that was known to be the most beautiful and luxurious on earth, was now merely heaps and mounds of ash. People stood by, looking at the giant monkey with the blazing tail, their houses and mansions burnt down,

Hanuman then plunged into the ocean putting out the fire on his tail. Then, assuming his normal form he made his way to Sita who was sitting under a tree. He fell at her feet and said, "Mother, your power is immense. Now allow me to go back to Lord Rama and tell him that you are safe, so that he can come and rescue you from the clutches of this demon, Ravana."

Sita blessed him with all her heart and gave him her jewels with great reverence to give to Lord Rama. With the jewels safely tucked away, Hanuman returned to the seashore, made himself as tall as a mountain and leaped across the mighty ocean.

The monkeys and bears awaiting his return on the other side, were overjoyed to see him flying back. On his arrival they picked him up and seated him upon their shoulders. After much celebration and shouts of joy, they made their way back to Sugreeva, their King.

On their way, they passed through a garden of many delicious fruits. The caretaker of this garden was Dadhimukha, brother of King Sugreeva. The Vanaras plundered the garden to rejoice the return of Hanuman. Soon Hanuman along with all the monkeys and bears reached Rama and Sugreeva.

Hanuman fell at Lord Rama's feet and said, "Lord, by your grace I have flown to Lanka and back. Princess Sita, the very embodiment of purity and chastity, says she will wait another month for you to rescue her from the clutches of the Demon King, Ravana. Here are the jewels she has given for you."

Lord Rama was beside himself with joy. He blessed and praised Hanuman on his bravery. Taking the jewels that Hanuman had brought he sat under a tree, his thoughts turned to the virtuous Sita. He could feel her anguish and agony, being alone in the city of the Demon King, Ravana. He thought about how she had managed to survive the torture that she was being subjected to. How would she brave the heat, the cold and the rain sitting under a tree? How did she stand the taunts of the demons and demonesses who visited her all the time?

After much anguish, Lord Rama's thoughts returned to the reality of the present moment. He wondered how he would manage the feat of crossing the deep and mighty ocean, with his army of monkeys and bears. He knew he had to cross the ocean along with the whole army to save Sita within a month, otherwise she might die in grief.

Lord Rama turned to Sugreeva and asked if he had any ideas on how to cross the ocean. Sugreeva thought for a long time and said, "Lord, Hanuman has already shown us that he can jump over the ocean. He can carry you and Prince Lakshmana on his shoulders and the rest of the army will reach Lanka somehow, do not worry about it. Give us the order to march to the ocean and we will cross it at any cost."

At noon that very day, Lord Rama gave the order to march to the seashore and the huge army of monkeys and bears set out. They carried Rama and Lakshmana on their shoulders. It was a long journey to the seashore riddled with forests, mountains and lakes but the army was enthusiastic and they marched at quite a fast pace. The thought of rescuing Princess Sita gave them added strength. Soon, they were at the seashore. Rama asked them to set up camp in the forest near the sea.

Looking towards the immense ocean, with its blue and white waves lashing the shore every moment, the monkey and bear army wondered how they would get across. Not all of them had powers to fly across like Hanuman could. They looked to Rama for direction who was also in deep thought. He was thinking of the ways and means by which that long stretch of ocean could be crossed.

Rama summoned all of the warriors and commanders and said, "I have been thinking about how to cross this ocean, and I have realised that it will need an ingenious solution. I want all of you to put your heads together. Remember, where there is a will, there is a way and when all of us put our will together, we will surely find a way." Rama's words gave them hope that they could somehow find a way to cross the ocean and rescue Sita.

The Bridging of The Ocean

After Lanka's destruction by Hanuman, Ravana was very worried. He was also angry at the thought that a mere monkey could have wrought such extensive damage to his beautiful city. He at once called a meeting of all his ministers and courtiers to chalk out the future course of action. As always, all his ministers praised him and told him that he was the mightiest of all demon kings and that no one could do him any harm. However, the doubt in Ravana's head was still not cleared.

So, he turned to Vibheeshana, his brother who always spoke the truth. Vibheeshana told him that unless they returned Sita to Lord Rama they would all perish. Ravana was livid with rage and would have killed Vibheeshana if he hadn't been his brother. Realising that Ravana would not see his own folly, and understanding that the truth was on Rama's side, Vibheeshana with four of his friends rose to the skies, flew across the ocean and took refuge with Lord Rama. Sugreeva was suspicious and thought Vibheeshana had come to spy on them. However, Lord Rama said that he would not turn away anyone who came to him for protection.

Sugreeva, Vibheeshana and Lakshmana then discussed strategy and devised techniques on ways to cross the mighty ocean, which was their greatest hurdle. Vibheeshana advised Lord Rama to start by praying to the God of the Sea. Rama was glad to accept his advice. He laid some grass on the seashore and started fasting and praying.

For three days, he prayed and fasted but his prayers seemed to have no effect. The sea god was unmoved. Lord Rama was beside himself with rage and got up to dry the seabed with his arrows of fire.

Taking up his mighty bow he fired a string of fiery arrows into the sea. The power of his arrows churned the sea and thunder and lightning flashed all around. The creatures of the sea ran helter-skelter, some took to the skies, some to the land. The noise was deafening and the bow continued to twang for a while.

As Lord Rama began to string another arrow onto his bow, the Sea God couldn't take it any more. The waters parted and shining like the radiant sun, the mighty God of the Sea appeared in all his magnificence.

He bowed to Rama and said, "Forgive me O, lord! I am but a slave to the laws of nature. All the five elements have to abide by the rules that nature has set down. By nature, I am supposed to be deep, full of waves and impassable which was why, I was unable to help you in any manner. However, now that I have been stirred, I will help you."

He continued, "There is an architect in the army of the Vanaras called Nala, the son of Viswakarma, the great architect. Let your army of monkeys and bears lay a bridge of wood and stones under his guidance. I shall hold it up for you and your army to cross." So saying, he bowed to Rama and vanished into the depths of the sea.

Heeding the advice of the God of the Sea, Rama summoned Nala and bestowed upon him the responsibility of constructing a bridge across the mighty ocean, over which the huge army of monkeys and bears could across to Lanka.

Nala bowed to Rama, thanked him for his trust and summoned all the monkeys and bears, asking them to uproot trees and collect rocks. They were to throw the trees systematically into the ocean and the God of the Sea would fulfil his promise and hold them up. Then they were to pave the bridge with rocks.

The monkeys and the bears enthusiastically set forth upon their task. They uprooted trees and laid rocks on them, and, wonder of wonders, the bridge of trees and rocks held up, floating on the mighty waters of the ocean. The bridge was 80 miles wide and stretched 800 miles, all the way to Lanka. They worked enthusiastically and hard, day and night and within a span of five days their passage to Lanka was ready.

As the strong monkeys and bears were building the bridge, a squirrel came out of the forest. Seeing that Lord Rama was building this bridge to cross the ocean, it came forward to help. The little squirrel pushed little bits of rock and sand into the sea, so the bridge could be stronger.

When Lord Rama saw the little squirrel doing its bit to help, he was very touched. He walked across and picked it up caressing it with his fingers. The power in his hands was so great that when he caressed the creature, the marks of his fingers were etched on its back. And that is how the squirrel got its stripes.

Finally, the bridge was in place and all the monkeys and bears romped in celebration, as the last stone was cast into the sea. Lord Rama was pleased as he looked upon this work of art. Gods, saints and sages showered their blessings upon the huge army of monkeys and bears.

Before they set off across the ocean, Rama prayed that their mission be a success. He then ordered the army to cross. The enthusiastic monkeys and bears ran to the bridge and with Rama and Lakshmana in the lead the long march to Lanka began.

The God of the Sea fulfilled his promise and held up the bridge crafted out of trees and rocks. The huge army walked across the bridge with no difficulty. Even though the monkeys and bears were tired after having worked hard on the bridge for many days, their spirits were high as they knew that Sita was in the land across the sea and they had to save her.

Their zeal and enthusiasm energized Rama and Lakshmana too. The march across the ocean was soon accomplished and they set foot on the golden banks of the land of Lanka, the abode of Ravana, the abductor of Sita. Their joy knew no bounds. They knew that having come this far they would surely rescue the Princess and reunite Rama and Sita.

Rama's army of monkeys and bears camped on the golden shores of Lanka with the peaceful, tranquil island spread out before them. The forests of Lanka were filled with fruits and roots that the monkeys and bears loved and with which they replenished their energy and their reserves of food.

When Ravana heard of the arrival of Lord Rama and his army to Lanka, he was very angry. He could not believe that they would cross the ocean and come over to Lanka in such a short span of time. In fact, he had not believed that they could cross the ocean at all! So, he sent for a demon magician named Vidhyut-Jiva and gave him orders to prepare an illusory head of Lord Rama. After the head of Lord Rama was prepared, Ravana went to see Princess Sita. When he showed the head to Sita she was completely beside herself with grief. She wept bitterly believing the illusory head to be the head of her beloved Lord Rama. Ravana took advantage of her in this weak moment and asked her once again if she would marry him. But the steadfast and virtuous Sita refused him at once.

When Sita refused him yet again, Ravana was beside himself with rage. He could not understand why this beautiful princess would choose a mortal like Rama over him, the King of all demons and the richest man on earth. He was also worried about Rama's army, which had reached his doorstep and went to the towers of his fort to see for himself. He saw the immense multitude on the shores of Lanka. The monkeys and bears taunted him and jeered at him to come and fight.

They danced and jumped up and down to instill fear in him. Though Ravana was now more fearful of Rama's strength, he showed none. In fact he scoffed and roared at the bears and monkeys. Little did he know that Rama was in fact much stronger than he thought he was and that the truth was on Rama's side. In a war of good against evil, good alone would triumph!

Attack On Lanka

Ravana stood on the ramparts of his fort and watched as the monkey and bear army surrounded his island kingdom. He was amazed and amused at the vast number of monkeys and bears that had come over in Rama's army to save Sita. How could this army of animals fight his army of strong and powerful demons? His laugh rang throughout the kingdom. On hearing this, the monkeys raised their heads and saw the demon king scoffing at them.

Sugreeva, standing by Rama's side was enraged to see the scorn that Ravana had just displayed. Not only was he angered by the demon king's disregard for the monkey and bear army, he was also incensed by the thought of the virtuous Sita, under the Rakshasa's roof. Red with rage, he sprang up and pounced on Ravana, knocking his crown off his head. Ravana was taken by surprise. The two kings fought, wrestling long and hard with each other. However, when Ravana resorted to trickery and magic, Sugreeva jumped back and returned to Rama's side.

Rama praised Sugreeva for his valour, but advised him not to take any such risks in the future. He also warned all his warriors that the battle would be fierce and they would have to fight with all their might. Rama could no longer tolerate Sita's plight at the hands of Ravana, and immediately ordered the monkeys and bears to attack the city of Lanka. They hurled rocks and boulders along with big tree trunks at the gates of Lanka which soon gave way.

When Ravana heard that the gates of Lanka had been broken open, he ordered his army to go to war. The demons rushed to the battlefield and a mighty battle ensued. The monkeys and bears used all their weapons, including their nails and teeth and tore the demons apart. The demons used their magical powers and killed many a monkey and bear. Hundreds of warriors fell on both sides. Rama and Lakshmana killed many demons with their sharp arrows. It was a fierce battle. Blood flowed in streams.

When Ravana saw that both the armies were evenly matched, he called his son Indrajit, a legendary warrior, and ordered him to go to the battlefield. Seeing Indrajit come to battle, the demons took heart and fought even more fiercely. Indrajit took on the brave Angada, when the latter came to the battlefield. Taking his cue, Jambumali, a demon general of Ravana, engaged Hanuman and Kumbhakarna's mighty son, Nikumbha fought with Neela, a monkey general in Sugreeva's army.

When Indrajit realised that the monkeys and the demons were evenly matched, he switched to sorcery. He made himself invisible and began showering arrows on the monkeys and bears from all sides. He also attacked Rama and Lakshmana. The two brothers aimed their arrows in different directions but Indrajit's shower of arrows continued unabated. Indrajit took advantage of his invisibility and shot serpent arrows at the Raghu brothers. The poisonous arrows found their mark and the brothers fell to the earth in a swoon. Indrajit roared with laughter as soon as he saw the two brothers fall.

As the monkey and bear warriors stood by the side of the fallen Raghu brothers, they wrung their hands in dismay. There was panic in Rama's camp. This was not something they had prepared for. As they stood, bewildered, Rama stirred. The effect of the poison from the serpent arrows had slowly worn off and Rama sat up weakly. There was a joyous cry among the ranks.

Rama held up his hand as Lakshmana was not yet awake. He gently lifted his brother's head and placed it on his lap. Sugreeva turned to Sushena, a physician from Lanka, for help to revive Lakshmana. However, the Gods were on their side. Just at that moment, Lord Vishnu's Garuda, rose from the mighty sea and at the first sight of the divine bird, the serpent darts vanished and Lakshmana rose. The monkeys and bears were delighted and they rushed back to the battlefield. When news of Rama and Lakshmana's revival reached Ravana, he was stunned. He decided that he would take to the battlefield himself and wipe the Raghu brothers off the face of the earth.

Before coming on to the battlefield, he had ordered Dhoomraksha a demon warrior, to go and kill the brothers. However, Hanuman made short work of Dhoomraksha and he was soon dead. Now Ravana was beside himself with rage. He rode out on his golden chariot, the very picture of a mighty warrior.

The earth trembled under the hooves of his horses. As he rode into the battlefield, he showered arrows on Rama's army. Hanuman and Neela were both defeated. Even Lakshmana could not fight the demon king and was felled. Then Rama, seated on Hanuman's mighty shoulders, faced Ravana. The battle was fierce. The earth shook under the force of the two warriors. Rama's arrows reached their marks. Ravana's crown fell and his chariot was smashed. His magnificent steeds were killed and his celebrated bow was broken to bits. He stood there on the battlefield, all alone, without a chariot or horses, without weapons or crown. Rama took pity on his state and said, "Ravana! You are indeed a brave warrior. Go back now and return tomorrow with new weapons."

Ravana hung his head in shame and shaking with fury and anger at being so humiliated, he returned to his palace. He had never faced defeat before and to meet defeat at the hands of an ordinary mortal made him feel terribly dejected. He went to his palace, held his head in his hands and sat thinking.

After a deep long thought, Ravana recouped his strength and asked for his brother, the giant Kumbhakarna to be roused from his sleep. Kumbhakarna was a giant of a demon, who ate for six months and slept for six months. Ravana knew that when Kumbhakarna awoke he would be hungry and angry. So, he made arrangements for vast quantities of food and meat, blood and wine to be placed near him. Elephants and men trumpeted loudly into Kumbhakarna's ears. The din continued for hours before the giant stirred. As soon as he awoke, he saw the food and ate for several hours, wiping every single dish clean. Then, he asked Ravana why he had been awakened. Ravana explained his plight and asked him to go to battle against Rama and Lakshmana.

Kumbhakarna picked up his mighty weapons and marched off to battle. He was so tall that his head seemed to touch the skies. He crushed men under his feet as he walked. As soon as he came on to the battlefield, the monkeys and bears took flight. They had never before seen such a giant of a man. Kumbhakarna crushed and devoured as many monkey and bear warriors as he could. With a single swipe of his weapon, he killed hundreds of warriors. Sugreeva and Angada, both fell to the ground.

Soon, Rama turned his attention to the giant Rakshasa who was causing such havoc. He shot sharp arrows at him and cut off his legs and arms. Thereupon the giant rolled about on the battlefield, crushing many monkeys and bears. Finally, Rama shot a powerful arrow and cut off Kumbhakarna's head. The force of the arrow carried the head several miles away. When Ravana heard of Kumbhakarna's death at the hands of Rama, he felt as if he himself had died. He had not expected this. Rama did not seem like an ordinary mortal anymore. Who was he?

Meanwhile, in Rama's camp, a great cheer broke out from the monkey and bear warriors. They rejoiced that the giant Rakshasa was no more, thanks to Rama's might. They knew that this was a turning point in the battle and with Rama by their side, they would win this war against the evil forces of Ravana. However, they realised that they had a long way to go and that Ravana would not give up or give in so easily, but they were also aware that whatever happened, truth alone would triumph. And the truth was on the side of the Raghu prince, Rama, who had come to save his divine consort, Sita, from the clutches of the evil demon, Ravana. The monkeys carried Rama and Lakshmana on their shoulders and danced joyously. They sang songs of the brothers' valour and wished each other luck in the forthcoming battle against Ravana and his forces of evil, which they would conquer for sure.

᙭ The Magical Sanjeevani ᙭

Rejoicing at their success, the monkey army gained new strength. They fought with renewed vigour, killing many hundreds of demon soldiers. The demon army took to its heels and the monkeys and bears raised their weapons to the sky in jubilation. However, their joy was short-lived, for soon enough, they saw Indrajit, the mighty warrior, the possessor of many magical powers ride out into the battlefield. He was not alone and beside him rode a wailing and weeping Sita. However, this was not the real Sita; it was an illusion that he had created with his magical powers, and Rama's army were not aware of this.

As he rode out and neared Rama's army, he pulled out his sword and killed the illusory Sita. The monkeys and bears were horrified and ran to narrate this tale of horror to Rama and Lakshmana. When Rama heard this he was greatly grieved. However, Vibheeshana, who was wise to Indrajit's tricks, consoled Rama and assured him that this was nothing but an illusion. Incensed by Indrajit's behaviour, Lakshmana prepared to ride out to battle against Indrajit.

Meanwhile, Indrajit was elated at having put Rama's army in a state of shock with his powers. He assured Ravana that he would take care of the Raghu brothers and that they would not be alive by the end of the day. So saying, he armed himself with all his weapons and rode out to battle again, launching a massive attack on Rama's army.

Lakshmana sought Rama's permission and blessings to fight Indrajit. Rama asked Hanuman and Angada to accompany him. When the two warriors came face to face, it was a battle of equals. Both Lakshmana and Indrajit could not outdo each other. Even though Indrajit used his magical powers time and time again, the enraged Lakshmana wanting to fight fair, killed Indrajit's charioteer and horses and smashed his chariot to pieces. Fearing for his life, Indrajit hurled the Brahmastra at Lakshmana. Lakshmana fell to earth in a swoon. When Rama heard of Lakshmana's fall, he immediately rushed to the battlefield. He was sorrow-stricken to see his brother wounded and in a swoon.

Grief-stricken and inconsolable, Rama sat on the battlefield, with Lakshmana's head on his lap. He wept bitterly. "I should never have allowed you to face that demon by yourself. Oh! What came over me?" he cried. All the monkey and bear warriors stood around the two brothers. It was Jambavan who took control of the situation as he knew what needed to be done. He said to Hanuman, "Fly north, O son of the Wind! Fly to the Himalayas. There you will find a hill of rare herbs between the peaks of Kailash and Rishabh. On this hill you will find the Mritasanjeevani, which can even bring a dead man to life. Bring this herb for Lakshmana and save his life. Only you can do it. Make haste. Go!"

Hanuman bowed to Jambavan's wise words and sought Rama's blessings. Rama blessed him and asked him to return as soon as possible saying, "My brother's life is in your hands, O Hanuman. Do come back with the magical Sanjeevani and save him. I will be indebted to you for life. Make haste!"

Hanuman took off in a giant leap and flew with great speed straight towards the Himalayas in the North, with Rama's words ringing in his ears. He had to get to the mountains and find the hill with the rare herbs. As he reached the foothills of the mountains, he saw the great peaks of Kailash and Rishabh rising up to the sky. He recollected Jambavan's words that the hill with the herbs was between the two great peaks. As he neared the mountains, he could see the hill and some of the herbs growing on it were shining with a divine light. As he descended he saw that the hill had many herbs in various colours and sizes. He was confused as to which was the Mritasanjeevani!

He looked around for a while, trying to figure out which of the herbs it was. Then he remembered Rama's words to make haste and made up his mind. Since, he could not recognise the wonder herb, he would take the whole mountain along. He prayed to Rama and then uprooted the hill with the herbs right off the ground. He leapt to the sky, with the hill held aloft and flew back towards Lanka.

As he neared the island kingdom of Ravana, the monkeys and bears, who were looking at the sky, waiting anxiously for his return were amazed at the sight of Hanuman carrying the whole hill back to Lanka. As he neared the camp, a great cheer went up from Rama's army. Hanuman descended, set the hill down and bowing to Rama he said, "Here I am, O Lord! Since I could not figure out which of the herbs was the magical Sanjeevani, and you had asked me to make haste, I have brought the whole hill." Rama was moved by Hanuman's heroic effort and embraced him.

In the meantime, Sushena had found the magical Sanjeevani amongst the various herbs. He picked out a few leaves, crushed them and held them to Lakshmana's nose. As soon as Lakshmana breathed in the magical fumes, he rose from his swoon. Rama embraced him warmly and wept with joy. The monkeys and bears sent a loud cheer into the skies. Lakshmana thanked Hanuman warmly for having saved his life. Hanuman bowed to him and said, "It is my duty, O Lakshmana. Think nothing of it!"

Meanwhile, Indrajit was making preparations for a yajna that would make him invincible, by which he could rout the forces of Rama and Lakshmana and give his father the victory he needed. He prayed with all his heart, performing many a sacrifice.

As the fires of the yajna rose to the skies, the monkeys in Rama's army got wind of Indrajit's plan. They decided to defile the yajna and render Indrajit's aspirations useless. Accompanied by Vibheeshana, Hanuman and the other monkey warriors went to the mountains where Indrajit was conducting his sacrifice. As Indrajit was about to complete his yajna and reap the benefits of his prayers, the monkeys defiled it by throwing things into the fire unsuitable for the yajna. Enraged at the defilement of his yajna and the futility of his prayers, Indrajit rushed to the battlefield and roared angrily at Rama's army.

When Indrajit came running out of his mountain abode, Lakshmana asked for Rama's blessings to challenge him once again in battle. Rama was hesitant but Lakshmana assured him that he would be all right. Praying to the gods to take care of his brother, Rama blessed him. Lakshmana challenged the roaring Indrajit who scoffed at him, "Haven't you had enough, you mortal? Do I have to use another astra on you?" Lakshmana roared back at him, "Come you sorcerer! I shall kill you today and teach your demon warriors a lesson. I will prove to you that truth alone will triumph!"

The battle was long and hard. It was fiercer than the last one. Both warriors used all their skills and were equally matched. Lakshmana destroyed Indrajit's chariot and killed his horses. However, Indrajit stood his ground. Demon though he was, he was also a mighty warrior who knew all the skills of battle. Lakshmana pulled out the Indra-astra and recalling Rama's blessings chanted the spell and let the astra fly.

The Indra-astra was a powerful weapon and Indrajit was not prepared for this onslaught. The astra flew straight, true to its mark, and cut Indrajit's head off. As soon as the rakshasa's head fell to the ground, the Devas showered flowers on the triumphant Lakshmana. Indrajit was dead. The mighty rakshasa had finally met his match in Lakshmana, who had proved that however strong the forces of evil, truth alone would triumph.

The monkeys and bears rushed to Lakshmana's side. With many a cheer, they carried him aloft on their shoulders to Rama's camp. There was great rejoicing. Rama embraced Lakshmana warmly and congratulated him on his glorious triumph. He said, "I know that we will win in the end. However, I am thankful to you for quelling such a great and evil force as Indrajit and proving to the world that truth alone triumphs." So saying, the two brothers reaffirmed their resolve to defeat Ravana and rescue Sita from his evil clutches.

Ravana's Fall

With the death of Indrajit, Ravana was shattered and felt that a part of him had died. He was the bravest of his sons and one on whom he depended greatly for support. Vacillating between shock and sorrow, Ravana wandered aimlessly around his palace, a pall of gloom everywhere.

He then thought of the other slain warriors and heroes in his camp. Retracing his mind to where this had all started he realised that it all began with Sita. Forgetting his vile behaviour and his insistence on abducting the Raghu princess, Ravana only thought of how she had been responsible for all the misfortune. He decided that if he killed her, his entire family would be avenged. As he set forth, with a mighty sword in his hands, his wise minister Suparsva stopped him and said, "O Ravana, what has happened to you? Sorrow has surely clouded your judgment. How can you kill a defenseless woman? How will you face yourself tomorrow? Prepare to fight Rama. It is only befitting that a great king like you meets a man in battle!"

Suparsva's words had their effect on Ravana and he stopped and held his head in his hands. "What am I doing?" he thought, and changed his mind. He called his army and enthused them with words of valour and encouragement. He ordered his soldiers and attendants to prepare him for battle. Riding a chariot that was swifter than the wind, he armed himself with the best weapons from his armoury. He called for his battle musicians and with the beating of the drums, rode out to battle.

There were many bad omens as he rode out to battle, but Ravana ignored them all as he was all charged up. The sight of Rama's banner inflamed him. He rode out with a giant roar, shooting his piercing arrows in many directions. He killed many monkey and bear warriors in his path. He was like the God of Death, never missing his aim as he goaded his army into ferocious battle with Rama's army. He vowed to finish off the monkey and bear soldiers at one go. Wrecking havoc wherever he went, he now searched for Rama.

In the meantime, innumerable monkeys and bears spilled forth from all directions, devastating the demon army. Rama also stood his ground. He fired arrows in every direction, till he was invisible, hidden by the volley of arrows that spilled forth from his mighty bow. Hanuman, Angada, Sugreeva, and Jambavan were also engaged in a mighty battle against the warriors from Ravana's army. They fought valiantly with Kumbhakarna's sons - Nikumbha and Kumbha. Yupaksha, Mahodara, Mahaparsva and Virupaksha, from Ravana's camp, also met the monkey and bear warriors in battle. The fighting was fierce and relentless.

Hanuman's mace flew from side to side destroying all in its path. Sugreeva claimed the honours by vanquishing the great Virupaksha and Mahodara. He fought with his bare hands, smashing with his fists and hurling rocks from one side to the other. Ravana looked around and saw all his brave warriors fall one by one. He realised that he had underestimated the strength of Rama's army. Dismissing them as a bunch of monkeys and bears had cost him the lives of his kith and kin.

Broken-hearted by the loss of so many soldiers and warriors, Ravana lost his nerve for a moment. He also thought of his brave son, Indrajit, killed by Lakshmana. As he thought of how many had died and how they had met their ends, Ravana's blood began to boil. His rage grew and he let out a giant roar. He was now more determined than ever to kill Rama and Lakshmana and avenge the death of his sons and kin.

Strengthened by his resolve, Ravana challenged Rama, "Fight with me, you mortal!" he cried. "I have waited for you, let me see what Sita sees in you that she refuses me, the greatest of the great kings! Is it your strength? How can it be more than mine, for I am matchless? Is it your valour? You are but a mortal and I am the King of demons! Come and fight with me! Let me see what strength and valour lies in that mortal form." Rama smiled at Ravana's taunts and replied, "I will fight you, Ravana! For I am here to show that good will always triumph over evil. Also, how can I forget the disrespect you have shown my Sita, by taking her away from me?"

Rama prepared to face him but the Raghu prince had no horses nor a chariot. He stood on the battlefield, with his bow and arrows and faced the mighty Ravana who was seated on a golden chariot driven by majestic steeds. When Vibheeshana asked Rama how he would fight Ravana without a chariot, he replied, "I am on a victory chariot, dear Vibheeshana. Look, Valour and Fortitude are its wheels. Truth and Virtue are on the banner of my chariot and its four mighty steeds are Strength, Prudence, Self-control and Benevolence. In its reins I hold Forgiveness, Compassion and an even mind. For the charioteer, I have the adoration of the greatest of the great - God. What about my weapons? Detachment is my shield, Contentment with what I have is my sword and Reason is the lance I hold. What else can I ask for? I have all that I need to battle with the mightiest of the mighty. I have truth on my side, that I can use to vanquish any evil that comes my way!" So saying, Rama stood his ground fearlessly. His army of warriors was amazed by his resolve and strength.

No sooner had Rama finished uttering these words, the Gods expressed that they were in praise of the Raghu Prince's conviction and strength by showering flowers upon him from the heavens. In accordance with the wishes of the other gods, Indra, the Lord of the Devas, sent his own divine chariot for Rama to use. The chariot was driven by the divine Matali, Indra's own charioteer. The four horses that pulled the chariot were invincible. It could fly as swiftly as a thought in the mind and was stronger than any other chariot.

As soon as the chariot landed, Rama and Lakshmana ascended it and took their places. The monkeys and bears were overjoyed and cheered loudly as Rama and Lakshmana rode the chariot into the battlefield. Strengthened with new vigour, the monkey and bear warriors also rushed into the battlefield, crushing the already dispirited demon soldiers. They razed everything that came their way and moved forward killing and devastating the demon army.

As Rama and Lakshmana rode out to battle on the divine chariot, Ravana also arrived at the battlefield, riding on his golden chariot pulled by eight horses. He shot off arrows from his bow like rain from the heavens. Many bear and monkey warriors were killed. Rama also shot arrows off his bow, in spells of metallic rain and they rendered all of Ravana's arrows futile.

Rama continued to shoot arrows at Ravana but they did not harm the demon-king at all. It was Matali, the charioteer, who called Rama's attention and said, "Lord, it is the Brahmastra alone that will work on this demon-king. Use it and watch him fall!" Rama heeded Matali's advice and pulled out the Brahmastra arrow. He chanted the spell and let the divine astra fly. Sure as lightning, the astra found its mark and pierced Ravana's giant chest. The life force flowed out of Ravana and he fell to the ground with a loud crash letting out a great groan. As his life ebbed, he uttered Rama's name for the first time, "O Rama!" Rama blessed him as Ravana breathed his last. Rama's blessing cleansed him of all his earthly sins and Ravana ascended to his heavenly abode.

There was a great cheer from Rama's army of monkey and bear warriors. The demon army was completely vanquished and not a single asura stood on the battlefield. The monkeys and bears dropped their weapons and rejoiced. They had achieved what they had come to Lanka for. Now all they needed to do was rescue Rama's divine consort, Sita.

Vibheeshana stepped forward, bowed to Rama and said, "My Lord, while I am full of grief at the demise of my brother, Ravana, I am also overjoyed at your victory over the forces of evil. Come with me, step into the city of Lanka and let your presence rid the land of any evil influence that might still be present." Rama replied, "Come Vibheeshana! I must now see my beloved Sita, for whom I fought this war. She is dearer to me than ever. Let me meet her as I have been away from her for too long." So saying Rama entered the city of Lanka, in anticipation of meeting his beloved, the virtuous Sita.

The Crowning of Vibheeshana

As Vibheeshana and Rama entered the city of Lanka through its massive golden gates, Vibheeshana swooned at the sight of his brother, Ravana's body. Rama raised him from the ground and said, "Do not grieve, Vibheeshana! His sins have all been forgiven and he has risen to the heavens. Perform his funeral rites, as befits the King of Lanka." Vibheeshana performed Ravana's last rites with all the respect due to him.

Vibheeshana then joined the Raghu brothers and they proceeded to the palace. Rama asked for preparations to be made for Vibheeshana to be crowned King of Lanka. The celebrations rang out through the city as the new King was crowned - one who stood for good and the truth. Even the Gods and the Devas were happy at the return of righteousness and virtue to Lanka. To show their appreciation, they showered flowers and blessings from the heavens. Amidst much pomp and grandeur, Vibheeshana ascended the throne of Lanka.

Now that Vibheeshana had been instated on the throne of Lanka, Rama asked Hanuman to proceed to the Ashoka garden and inform Sita that Ravana was killed in battle. Hanuman, on reaching the Ashoka Garden, bowed to Sita and conveyed the news to her. She was overcome and shed tears of joy.

Rama then asked Vibheeshana to send a palanquin to bring Sita from the garden to the palace. When Sita was brought to the palace, with all the respect that was due to her, the monkeys and bears were overjoyed. As she descended from the palanquin, Rama was elated to see his beloved after such a long time. Though he felt sad at the troubles and tribulations she had gone through, he was also happy to have her back at last. However, Rama knew that he could not accept Sita before she satisfied many future doubts that people might have. So he said to her, "Sita! You will have to step into the burning fire to establish your chastity and purity!"

Sita accepted her lord's demands, for she knew that Rama would not ask her for anything that was not right or just. She also knew that as the epitome of virtue, he had to set an example for all the others. So she said to Lakshmana, "Please light a fire for me!" Lakshmana knew that this ordeal was necessary but he was saddened that Sita's troubles were still not over, and lit a fire for Sita.

With a prayer on her lips and faith in her heart, Sita said to the God of Fire, "Prove to the world that I am as pure as you are. If I have sinned even in my dreams, burn me to ashes!" So saying she stepped into the fire. There was a gasp from all gathered. Here was a princess delicate as a flower, now right in the middle of a huge flame, unscathed and untouched. The flames leaped about her, burning bright and the heat seared the faces of all those standing nearby. However, Sita remained amidst the flames, her hands together in prayer and her self unaffected by the fire in any manner.

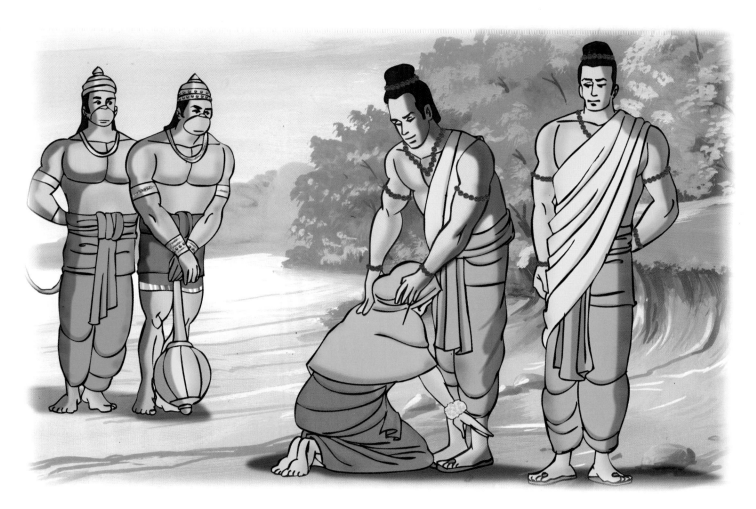

As soon as Sita stepped out of the fire as beautiful as ever, she bowed at Lord Rama's feet. He bent and raised her, embracing her warmly. Not even for a moment had he doubted her but now he had effectively quelled all doubts that others might have of her purity and chastity. He said to her, "Do not take to heart what I said and asked you to do, my beloved Sita. I have put to rest all the doubts that the world might have of you! I have proved to the world that you are the epitome of purity and chastity. No one can now have any doubts about you."

Dasharatha's spirit descended from the heavens and blessed Rama, Lakshmana and Sita. Rama sought forgiveness for Queen Kaikeyi and asked him to take back his curse that disowned the Queen and Prince Bharatha. Dasharatha agreed and Rama bowed to him seeking his blessings for their journey back to their motherland, Ayodhya, as his period of exile was now over. He was full of hope and anticipation and was eager to meet his beloved mothers and brothers.

As preparations were being made for Rama's return to Ayodhya with his beloved wife and brother, Indra descended from the heavens. He blessed Rama for freeing the earth from the burden of the evil king Ravana. He said, "The whole earth rejoices at your victory. Now, make a wish and we will see to it being fulfilled!" Rama asked him to bring to life all the monkeys and bears killed in battle. No sooner had Indra nodded his head, the monkeys and bears came back to life, amidst the cheers of all.

Then the Raghu Princes and Princess ascended the Pushpaka Vimana - the flying chariot - to fly to Ayodhya. Sugreeva, Hanuman, Angada, Jambavan and the huge army of monkeys and bears accompanied them. They passed all the places where they had been - Kishkindha, Panchavati and the ashrams of the Sages. As they reached the hermitage of Sage Bharadwaja, they sent word to Bharatha of their return. Soon Ayodhya was in sight. Rama was overjoyed to see the land of his birth and was keen to meet his mothers and other brothers.

As soon as word of Rama, Lakshmana and Sita's return reached Ayodhya, the entire land erupted in joy. There were celebrations everywhere. The joy of the people knew no bounds. Happiness once again returned to their motherland and they rejoiced like never before. To welcome the Princes and the Princess, the city of Ayodhya was decorated with no efforts spared. Flowers decked every nook and corner of the city. Lamps were lit everywhere, till the place glittered and gleamed like a bride. The fragrance of the flowers and their vibrant colours brought cheer to every soul.

As they neared Ayodhya, Rama, Sita and Lakshmana descended from the Pushpaka Vimana and set forth on foot. The army of rejoicing bears and monkeys followed them. They could see the entire city lit up in welcome and also saw the garlands of flowers that adorned every corner of the place. The people of Ayodhya rushed out to shower flower petals. Soon the returning Princes and Princess and the victorious army was walking on a pathway of flowers.

As soon as the joyous procession neared Ayodhya, Bharatha rushed out to meet his beloved brothers and his sister-in-law. For fourteen years, he had ruled the kingdom in the name of his brother Rama, counting each passing day. He had ruled justly and righteously, taking decisions as Rama would have. His sorrow at having his elder brother live in the forest was so great that Bharatha had been living like a hermit in Nandigram, outside Ayodhya. Now that he knew Rama was back, his heart overflowed with joy. He hastened to the palace, telling one and all that Rama, Lakshmana and Sita were back.

Then he rushed to meet the approaching procession. He ran to Rama and fell at his feet, his tears washing the lotus feet of the Lord and said, "You cannot imagine how glad I am to have you back!" Rama was touched. He raised Bharatha and embraced him warmly. Bharatha also embraced Lakshmana and sought Sita's blessings. Then he led the three of them into the city of Ayodhya. The people showered flowers on them from rooftops and terraces and chanted Rama's name with a joy never known before.

Upon hearing of the return of Rama, Sita and Lakshmana, the entire palace had sprung to life. Darkness vanished as lamps were lit. A fresh breeze blew through the rooms of the palaces. The three Queens, till now in mourning, greeted one another in joy. The guards decorated the palaces and lit lamps. The maids-in-waiting distributed sweets for all. The three Queens rushed to welcome the Princes and the Princess.

As soon as Rama, Sita and Lakshmana entered the main palace, Queen Kaushalya, Queen Kaikeyi and Queen Sumitra welcomed them with lamps in their hands and tears in their eyes. Rama, Lakshmana and Sita fell at the feet of the Queens and sought their blessings. They were then escorted into the palace and with them joy returned to the land of Ayodhya!

Rama's Coronation

With the return of the Princes Rama and Lakshmana and the Princess Sita to Ayodhya after being in exile for fourteen years the joy and celebration in the kingdom of Koshala continued for days together.

Bharatha was also much relieved and happy that Rama was now back to take his rightful place on the throne of Ayodhya. For the last fourteen years, he had placed Prince Rama's sandals on the floor of the throne and on his behalf had righteously ruled over and looked after the kingdom and people of Ayodhya.

Rama, Sita and Lakshmana on arriving in the palace caught sight of the noble Sages Vashishta and Vamadeva. They laid down their weapons at once and bowed down to be blessed by the Sages. Everyone in the kingdom was happy as Bharatha led them into the palace followed by the two Sages, Vashishta and Vamadeva.

The Sages Vashishta and Vamadeva assembled together all the learned scholars and other sages of the kingdom to decide on a date for the coronation of Lord Rama. On studying the astrological charts, it was unbelievably found that the time was right for Lord Rama to be crowned as King on that very day. Lord Rama, Lakshmana and Princess Sita bathed and donned their regal robes. The clothes of Lord Rama were embellished richly with precious gems, stones and jewels. The three Queen-Mothers dressed Sita in fine clothes and jewellery. Then, Lord Rama and Sita were led to the royal throne.

The great Sage Vashishta placed the crown on Lord Rama's head and proclaimed him the king of Koshala. All the sages who had gathered, blessed Lord Rama and Princess Sita. Kaushalya, Sumitra and Kaikeyi distributed gifts of gold and clothes to the poor and the needy. There was celebration like never seen before in the kingdom. The people rejoiced at the return of happiness after so long!

Many months after Lord Rama had been crowned King he called all the monkeys who had followed him to Ayodhya and said, "You have served me well and helped fight with the Demon King Ravana and his army to bring back Princess Sita. Now, it is time for you to return to your home, but always bear in mind that you will always remain dear to me."

He gave them his blessings and showered them with many gifts. Hanuman, the chief minister of Sugreeva was intent on staying with Lord Rama to serve him for all eternity. Lord Rama repeatedly told him to return to his home but he refused to leave Rama's side. In order to prove that Lord Rama was dear to him he tore open his chest with his bare hands to reveal Lord Rama and Sita sitting upon a throne in his heart. Sugreeva was wonder struck at this devotion and allowed Hanuman to stay and serve Lord Rama. Hanuman thanked Sugreeva and fell at Rama's feet asking for nothing but to be allowed to remain at the foot of Rama's throne. Rama blessed him.

For the day-to-day governance of the kingdom, Lord Rama appointed many spies to report to him about all that was happening in the kingdom. One day, one of his spies whose name was Bhadra came to see Lord Rama. Rama asked him about the status of his subjects and if they were happy under his reign. Bhadra replied that his subjects were happy, and were in admiration of Lord Rama for building a magnificent bridge across the sea to go to Lanka and destroy the mighty demon King Ravana.

He continued, "However, O Lord, they also think that it was wrong on your part to have accepted Princess Sita back after she had lived with the vile Ravana for so long, which renders her to be impure. They feel that she is not fit to live in the palace." Lord Rama was very troubled by this. He sat brooding for a long time over this. He wondered how he would address this issue that his subjects were troubled about. He knew that no amount of convincing would make them believe in Sita's purity and chastity.

Lord Rama knew that Sita was pure and chaste, but he realised that there was no way to pacify his subjects about this. Being King, he had to set an example. Sita would have to be sent away from the palace. He sent for his brothers Lakshmana, Bharatha and Shatrughna and as soon as they had gathered he said, "I do not have any doubt in my mind about the purity of Sita. It has been made clear that Sita is pure and faultless by the God of fire, Agni himself. However, the people of Ayodhya do not consider her fit to live in the palace. They say that she is a bad example and that their wives may be influenced to follow in her footsteps."

Then he turned to Lakshmana and said, "It is my wish that you take Sita to the opposite bank of the Ganga and leave her near the hermitage of the great Sage Valmiki." Though it was a sad decision, the brothers accepted Rama's judgement and his belief that there was no other way to dispel the doubt that had formed in the minds of the subjects.

Lakshmana was grief-stricken that he had to leave Sita in the forest but he was bound by his duty to Lord Rama. The next morning, with Sita seated in the chariot, he drove out to the opposite bank of the Ganga, near the hermitage of the great Sage Valmiki as Lord Rama had instructed.

He stopped the chariot and after Sita alighted he said, "Lord Rama has asked me to leave you near the hermitage of Sage Valmiki. I am grief-stricken at having to do this but it is my brother's command. The subjects of Ayodhya do not have a good impression and they doubt your purity and nobility. Hence, Lord Rama has instructed me to leave you here so you may live in the hermitage of Sage Valmiki, the friend of my father Dasharatha."

On hearing this, Sita was completely overwhelmed with sadness and wept in grief. However, she said, "If Lord Rama has instructed you to leave me here then abide by your duty and I also will do as my Lord wishes."

So Lakshmana left her and with much sadness in his heart made his way back to the palace. Meanwhile, Sita sat on the shore and cried to herself, as she was grief-stricken. The hermits who lived in the hermitage of the great Sage Valmiki noticed her and felt very sad. They went to the Sage and told him that they had seen a woman sitting on the bank of the Ganga and crying.

The Sage went to Sita and said to her, "I know you. You are Sita, the daughter-in-law of the great King Dasharatha and the wife of Lord Rama. I know that you have been sent to live with me, as the subjects of Ayodhya doubt your purity. But I have no doubts about you; I know that you are faultless. Please come to my hermitage where I will take good care of you. Bear no worry in your heart." So saying he asked her to accompany him to the hermitage and live within the peaceful domain that he had in the forest.

Sita was reassured by the words of the great Sage. She gained confidence and rose, wiping her tears with the edges of her robes. As she made her way to the hermitage with the great Sage Valmiki, her anxiety lessened and though her heart was filled with sorrow, she became much stronger in her resolve to follow Lord Rama's wishes and stay in the forest.

The people living in the hermitage greeted Sita warmly. The ladies of the hermitage welcomed her and made her feel better. She did not now feel as lonely as she had been on the banks of the Ganga. Living in the hermitage was going to be yet another new experience for her but she prepared herself for the new life ahead. She knew that this was all a part of a greater plan. Soon, she became accustomed to the life in the hermitage and helped with the chores. Sita settled down peacefully, thinking of her Lord Rama all the time!

The Sons of Rama

Sita lived happily in the hermitage of the great Sage Valmiki under the loving care of the women there. She found peace and forgot her sorrows, though she thought of her Lord Rama all the time. One day Shatrughna, on his way to fight the demon Lavana stopped to rest in Sage Valmiki's hermitage for the night. On that very same night Sita gave birth to two sons. Sage Valmiki on being informed of the birth of the twin boys, visited her and was overjoyed on seeing the two babies. Shatrughna was also very happy that he had become an uncle.

With all the people living in the hermitage gathered around the newborn babies, the great Sage Valmiki picked up the babies one at a time and named them. He named one baby Lava and the other Kusha. Valmiki was also happy to see that Sita had gotten over her grief. Sita now spent all her time, looking after and playing with her sons.

With the birth of the two boys, the sons of Rama, the great Sage Valmiki spent most of his time training them in the ways of how to rule a kingdom and the art of war. He was a very learned sage, well versed in the scriptures as well as in the art of war. His knowledge was respected all across the land and he also had the power to see into the future. Under his expert guidance and training the boys, Lava and Kusha, learnt quickly and soon they were accomplished warriors.

Sita also saw to it that they paid attention to their lessons. She was very happy with the way her sons were growing up in the capable hands of Valmiki. They were educated meticulously in the scriptures. By the time they reached adolescence, they were also very skilled at archery and other weaponry, and were better than any seasoned warriors.

Meanwhile, in Ayodhya, Lord Rama wanted to perform the Ashwamedha yajna. This yajna would establish his supremacy all across the land. A horse would roam from kingdom to kingdom with an army designated by Rama. The king who dared stop or challenge the horse, would have to fight Rama's army. On the other hand whoever let the horse pass would have to accept Rama as Lord and master.

Rama asked Lakshmana to invite all the noble sages to perform this yajna. Lakshmana called the Sages Vashishta, Vamadeva, Jabali and Kashyapa to prepare for the yajna. Lord Rama sent messengers in all directions to inform and invite sages and saints, and kings and princes. King Vibheeshana, Janaka and Sugreeva graced the yajna. A beautiful golden statue of Sita was placed to the left of Lord Rama as no holy yajna could be performed without the presence of the wife. Thousands of people attended the yajna. A very beautiful horse adorned from head to toe and decked with jewels stood next to the fire.

As soon as the yajna was complete, the horse was released. A declaration tied around its neck said in bold letters "This horse belongs to the emperor of the kingdom of Kosala, Shri Rama. Whoever captures this horse will have to wage a war with him. Those who let the horse pass, thereby accept his Lordship and will have to start paying taxes."

Shatrughna followed the horse from a distance heading the huge army, ready to fight anyone daring enough to capture the horse. No one dared to touch the horse as they travelled for a long time, across many a kingdom and land. All the kings and princes accepted Rama's supremacy and gave Shatrughna rich presents to take to Rama.

One day, the horse passed through a dense part of the forest where the hermitage of the great Sage Valmiki was situated. The twin brothers Lava and Kusha were fascinated by the beautiful white steed. They captured it and tied it to a tree. When they read the declaration tied around its neck, they waited eagerly for its defenders to face them.

It was not long before the army that was following the horse appeared. Seeing that Lava and Kusha had captured the horse they asked the boys politely to release it. Lava and Kusha refused and challenged a fight. The soldiers laughed since they were just boys but soon under the intense attack of the twins, they realised that they were not dealing with two ordinary boys, but warriors of great skill and expertise.

Lava and Kusha laid to waste most of the army, and the soldiers that lived, ran back to Shatrughna to inform him of the attack. Shatrughna came to see the two amazing boys for himself. As he approached the twins, he asked them to stop playing and return the horse. However, the boys replied with their arrows and soon Shatrughna was fighting them, trying to keep them back with much difficulty. The twins attacked him so fiercely that soon he fell to the ground unconscious. The soldiers, seeing that the two boys had defeated Shatrughna ran away in panic.

The fleeing soldiers ran to Lord Rama and informed him about the havoc that had taken place. Rama was surprised to hear that two boys had defeated Shatrughna, his brother, the slayer of foes. He sent Lakshmana to fight the twins but cautioned him not to kill them but to capture them alive. As soon as Lakshmana saw the two boys, he was surprised that they had felled Shatrughna, as they looked so innocent and small. He decided that he would appeal to their good sense first and asked them to release the horse, but in vain.

The twins drew Lakshmana into a fight. Lakshmana was finding it very difficult to fight the twins as they kept showering him with their sharp arrows. He mustered all his strength and shot a mighty arrow at Kusha who was overpowered and swooned. However, by his powers of meditation he came out of his swoon and resumed fighting. Meanwhile, Lava showered Lakshmana with many arrows to keep him in check. One of his arrows found its mark and Lakshmana fell down in a faint.

When the news that Lakshmana had also been defeated was conveyed to Lord Rama by his soldiers he was annoyed and sent Bharatha and Hanuman to fight. Bharatha put up a good effort but the twins were too much for him to handle. When Lord Rama heard that Bharatha had also been overpowered by the twins he came to fight them himself.

However, when he looked at them, and saw their innocent faces he couldn't bring himself to fight. He asked who their parents were because they didn't look like warriors. The twins replied that their mother was the daughter of King Janaka of Mithila.

Lord Rama was overjoyed to hear this. His army had been fighting his sons all this while! Lava and Kusha asked Lord Rama to fight them and shot arrows at him. However, he only defended himself against their onslaught and did not fight back. The great Sage Valmiki had been noticing the turn of events and soon stepped out to put an end to the fighting.

As soon as Lord Rama saw the great Sage Valmiki, he dropped all his weapons and fell at his feet to seek his blessings. The great Sage blessed Lord Rama and informed him that Lava and Kusha were indeed Rama's own sons. Lava and Kusha looked at their father, and happily rushed into his arms.

Then the great Sage Valmiki narrated to Lord Rama how he had given shelter to the pregnant Sita. He added that the twins were born in his hermitage and had been tutored to be brave warriors. Lord Rama was very happy and he took Lava and Kusha with him to live in the palace and rule by his side. Thus the sons of Rama went to Ayodhya to live and rule in the tradition of the great Raghu dynasty.